Katherine Bar⋯ ⋯eries 'L⋯
of Eve'. She ⋯ NAPIER UNIVE⋯ LEARNING INFORMAT⋯ a produc⋯
Woman's H⋯ ⋯ maga⋯ne p⋯ogrammes. In television, ⋯
made progr⋯ ⋯es such as 'Rough Guide to the World' for ⋯ 2,
'Move Over Darling', for BBC 1 and 'The Thing Is . . . Christma⋯ for
Channel Four.

D1634510

LABOURS OF EVE

Katherine Barnby

B◼XTREE

First published in Great Britain in 1995 by Boxtree Limited

Text © Katherine Barnby 1995

The right of Katherine Barnby to be identified as Author of this work has been asserted by her in accordance with the Copyright, Designs and Patents Act 1988.

1 2 3 4 5 6 7 8 9 10

Cover designed by Sarah Hall
Typeset by SX Typesetting
Printed and bound in Finland by WSOY for

Boxtree Limited
Broadwell House
21 Broadwell
London SE1 9PL

A CIP catalogue entry for this book is available from the British Library.

ISBN 1 85283 947 3

Front cover illustration: *La Vie* (1903) by Pablo Picasso,
© The Cleveland Museum of Art/DACS

Acknowledgements

I would like to thank Tessa Livingstone, whose idea *Labours of Eve* was, for the opportunity to work on both the TV series and this book; also, Susan Spindler and Angela Holdsworth, who have guided the series throughout. I am very grateful to Nicky Singer, the presenter of the series, and directors Polly Bide, Lucy Hannah, Kathy O'Neil, Deborah Perkin, Emma Swain and particularly Lyn Webster Wilde for all the great conversations we have had about infertility and reproductive medicine. Extra research was provided by Chandra Paul Leo, Miranda Christians, Fiona Morris, Laura Ponti Sgargi, Valerie Patten and Judith Hagerty. Many thanks also to Penny Simpson and Susanna Wadeson at Boxtree, Julian Alexander, and Professor Robert Winston for editing the medical parts of the book.

For putting up with the massive inconvenience of living with a book, I would like to thank Michael and Roselle Phelan, Margaret and Leslie Barnby and my sisters Alison, Tessa and Sally. Most of all, I would like to thank the women who agreed to contribute – Miranda, Liz, Sheila, Vivienne, Laura, Rosemary and Helen – and all the many other people I interviewed over the last year.

Contents

Foreword
by Nicky Singer

When the BBC was seeking a presenter for the 'Labours of Eve' series they contacted my publishers, Virago, who told them I had just written a novel dealing with infertility. The characters and the plot of *To Have and to Hold* are fictitious. The pain is not. For twenty months I tried and failed to conceive a child. This experience and the way in which I handled it (badly) taught me something of the passions involved. But nothing could have prepared me for the intensity of sharing the lives and stories of the six women with whom we filmed, and the women whose testimony is recorded in this book.

Those of us who are now in our child-bearing years are probably the first generation to be brought up with the pill and feminism as givens. The pill gave us freedom from unwanted pregnancies and feminism the freedom to be what we wanted: individuals, career women as well as wives and mothers. Implicit in the deal were certain assumptions: that we were all fertile (why else did we need 98% effective contraception?); and that we gained rather than lost (in terms of maturity and financial security) if we delayed our child-bearing. Delay was also expected of us. Our mothers were inadequate if they weren't just mothers, we were inadequate if we weren't something more. We found out only when the ticking of the biological clock became impossibly loud, that fertility declines rapidly with age. Only 7 per cent of those unsuccessfully trying to conceive in their early twenties remain infertile. This figure rises to 33 per cent at thirty-five and 60 per cent at forty. Naive as it sounds, if we were shocked to discover at thirty that we wanted babies, we were stunned to realize we might never have them.

Ours is an age which prides itself on the ascendancy of the rational over the biological. It is difficult to express the obsessional nature of the desire for a child without sounding faintly mad. But then I think there is a madness involved – the madness of grief. Just as women cry for miscarried children (and they are children, not foetuses) I think it is possible to cry for the unborn, to mourn the loss of a child who may never be. Whether this is rational or not is beside the point. This is the power of the emotions involved. However, while the grief which goes with death is recognized and respected, the grief that accompanies infertility is often not. Sometimes the only place for its expression is

1

between the couple themselves. And, just as different people grieve for a death differently, so it is with infertility. The experience may bring a couple together, but it may also drive them painfully apart.

The ability to procreate is one of the most fundamental aspects of man the animal. Not to be able to be 'fruitful and multiply' strikes at the heart of our being. It sets the infertile apart. Not just different, but lesser. Having babies is so basic, so natural, that not to be able to conceive makes the infertile feel 'un-natural', freakish, isolated from the core of life and the children who seem, when you're not pregnant, to be everywhere about you.

The taboo, the isolation of infertility (as in many things concerning sex) is also to do with shame. If you can't run very well because you have asthma, that is a problem with a value-free explanation. If you can't conceive easily because of endometriosis, or immature sperm, that is a matter for secrecy and humiliation. It un-mans or un-womans us, makes us failures. It's often difficult for outsiders to grasp the nature of this sense of failure, which is as profound as the stakes are high. 'Pull your socks up.' 'Stop brooding.' 'Take a holiday.' It's hard to take a holiday from your body, to try and forget its rhythms and cycles, its lunar bleeding. 'Why do you want a child so much anyway?' Nobody asks this of a fertile couple.

There is also a second sort of failure many women experience – a failure of control. We learn as children that being grown-up means being in charge, being in control. Infertility undermines this completely, because no matter what you are prepared to sacrifice or to risk, you never know when – or if - you will ever have a child. You remain in limbo, poised perfectly between hope and despair. It is an unnerving place to be. It also explains, I think, why women can become obsessional about charts and dates and timings, they – we – are attempting to take control of the small things, having lost control of the big ones.

Of course we go for help. We turn to doctors, to medicine. We place our broken bodies in their hands and say 'fix me'. And sometimes they can. Since the 'test-tube' birth of Louise Brown in 1978, there has been a proliferation of technologies to aid reproduction. Their success rate is variable and always – statistically – low. But any chance of success is a chance worth taking for the infertile. And often enough, after drugs, or surgery, or IVF, there is born a child who, for the parents, will always be the supreme gift, in Laura Edwards' words 'an utter miracle'. Sometimes it's not so simple. The hi-tech GIFT treatment gave Helen Pusey the chance of children. At what terrible cost is told in this book.

Why do we put our faith in doctors? Because of a potent cocktail of ignorance (ours – they are the experts) and need. Desperation leads people to be more trusting, ask fewer questions and take greater risks than they might ordinarily do. But the experts can be right and they can be wrong.

2

Rosemary Thornton was told her insides 'looked like a butcher's shop' and that she would never conceive. Three months later she was pregnant, albeit a pregnancy she was later to miscarry. The truth is that, despite all we know about fertility, much of it is still uncharted territory. Medicine cannot explain 'waiting-list' pregnancies, or why there is a rise in the incidence of conception in the three months after a laparoscopy. Yet we beg our doctors to know. We also surrender to the knowledge that they do have. If something is medically possible we often don't stop to question whether it is right morally.

In the sixteen years since the birth of Louise Brown we have gone from the revolutionary, but 'natural' fertilization of eggs outside the womb to ICSI – intracytoplasmic sperm injection. In this procedure the doctor selects a single sperm and uses microinjection to place it actually inside the body of the egg. Leaving aside the question of possible congenital abnormalities (there have been too few cases to date to make up a proper research study) there is an ethical question involved. Is it right for doctors – for us – to play God in this way? The infertile woman is not, I think, in a position to make an uncoloured choice. I remember being so consumed that I don't think I'd have cared what I did to achieve a pregnancy. But we must care for the sake of the children. What, taking another instance, should we tell children born by artificial insemination by donor? Will they seek their sperm fathers to resolve questions of their own identity? We don't know the answer to this because the children are, as yet, too young to ask.

About 15 per cent of couples will experience infertility at some point in their lives. With overpopulation of the world a serious issue, it's difficult to be sympathetic. With medical resources under such pressure, it's difficult to be sympathetic. It's often difficult to be sympathetic with the infertile themselves: it's one of our guilts, how selfish we can be, how intolerably we can behave. But I think society owes the infertile a duty of care, because society must care about the moral issues, because we underestimate biological need at our peril, and because each individual that makes up that 15 per cent is a human being in pain.

I never cried so much as I did during the making of the 'Labours of Eve' series. I listened to heartbeats and the hope of heartbeats. I sat with women who would never be mothers and mothers who had cradled their infants in the palms of their hands and watched them die. I saw joy which had been carved from a rock-face of pain and I witnessed the women themselves – their extraordinary emotional honesty, their brutal courage. I salute each one of them. And I thank them for speaking out, for breaking the taboo. We all learn that we must deal with our own griefs in our own ways. But we need not do it in secret. And we need not do it alone.

3

Introduction

When researching the television series 'Labours of Eve', I spoke to hundreds of women about their experiences of infertility. I realized that one of the reasons so many people contacted the programme was because there are so few opportunities to talk about not having children. It was a revelation to me how deeply affected many women remained, but also how little of the real trauma of infertility is reflected in the publicity IVF and other treatments receive.

This book is published with the intention of helping women who may be worrying about their fertility. The seven women featured here describe their feelings about their bodies, their status as women, the strength of their desire for children, the highs and lows of fertility treatment, how they dealt with the doctors and the significance these events played in their lives at the time they were undergoing treatment. I hope that it will answer many questions I wanted answered, such as, the effect the treatment might have on a relationship or what a course of hormonal drugs which stimulate the ovaries really feels like.

It is a guide to the emotional experience of infertility rather than a medical guide. (Professor Robert Winston's book *Getting Pregnant* is an excellent book which explains all the technical details about fertility treatment.) In the text I have given explanations of medical terms and treatments where necessary.

The experiences of these women are all very individual and as different personalities they deal with situations in various ways. They all agreed to make a contribution because they wanted to share their knowledge with other women and also because they felt that a book like this would have been useful to them.

The idea for the television series was conceived by Tessa Livingstone who is a Series Producer in the Science and Features Department of the BBC. She wanted to make a series which looked behind the great excitement which has accompanied the advances in reproductive technology such as IVF and microsurgery. The television series took a much broader brief and looked at subjects such as abortion and surrogacy. This book focuses simply on the experience of infertility and the medical treatments which have been developed to treat it. Only Helen's story features both as a film and in the book because it was about multiple birth as a result of GIFT.

The similarity between the TV series and the book is that each woman tells her own story. People sometimes refer to fertility treatment as 'The IVF Game'. The process is rather like snakes and ladders, with, for example, a diagnosis of endometriosis forcing you to miss eight months of menstruation, or a poor egg collection sending you back to square one. The final aim is obviously a baby and the majority of players never get to the end.

The experiences the women describe start from the time they first considered the idea of children. The following are some short biographies which describe the other parts of their lives and how important having children had been to them before they knew they might have problems conceiving.

Miranda Walsh

After university Miranda began a career as a project manager working in a design company. She was thinking about an alternative career which would be more compatible with children but not mean a huge drop in status. She chose to become a homeopath and studied the first two years of the course in her spare time. During the third year the recession began and she left the company to study full time. She now practises homeopathy in north London.

Despite her lack of enthusiasm for the rat race, Miranda would describe herself as a very ambitious person. She is keen to achieve a lot in homeopathy and glad to be able to pursue her own goals rather than those set down by the requirements of a company.

Miranda's intention all through early adulthood was to have her children before she was thirty. Her mother had become pregnant instantly she had unprotected sex and Miranda assumed she would be much the same. Clive, her husband, also felt confident that they could plan a pregnancy to fit in with the rest of their lives. They met early in their twenties and were one of the first couples among their group to think about children. Miranda, particularly, feels she has built her whole life and her idea of herself around having children and a profession.

Cause of Infertility: Polycystic ovaries.

Liz Morris

Liz Morris is a public relations consultant in London. After taking a degree in English she was employed in an advertising agency for about seven years, working on accounts for Mars, WH Smith, Pernod and Lurpak butter. Her social life was fairly extensive and work was hard and time-consuming.

Around this time Liz was singing Blues and Tamla Motown songs in a band. The bass player was called Andy. They had met before because he was also an Art Director in the agency they both worked for, but at that time Liz had been engaged to her previous husband. They spent the summer debating whether to risk a brilliant friendship by letting it become a sexual relationship, eventually married and have never looked back. They started to think about having children when Liz was about twenty-eight.

Her mother had Liz when she was thirty-two and her other two children at thirty-four and thirty-six. Consequently she never put pressure on Liz about having a family because for her it was normal to have children later. Her mother has always been sensitive and understanding about infertility.

Liz doesn't ever remember babies being around when she was a child. The first time she was aware of meeting a baby was when she was twenty-eight and a friend from university had one. Then suddenly the world seemed to be filling up with them. For Liz it was her relationship with Andy that made her want to have a child.

Cause of Infertility: Possible lack of ovulation, low sperm count.

Sheila Rogers

Sheila teaches in a further education college in Edinburgh. She met and married her husband, who is also a teacher, in 1984 when she was thirty. During her twenties she had been very career-oriented and had never experienced any craving to have children. She felt very strongly that it was important that women should work, even to the extent of feeling sorry for those who didn't. She feels she resisted sex, up until her marriage, because of a fear of getting pregnant, probably owing to her Catholic upbringing.

She and her husband started to try for children about a year into their marriage.

Cause of Infertility: Endometriosis, lack of ovulation, low sperm count.

Vivienne Howard

Vivienne is a qualified nurse but now works as a bereavement counsellor. She spent the time between leaving school and starting her nursing training, in Torbay in 1973, as a nanny because she had a great rapport with children. In 1977 she decided to join the Royal Army Nursing Corps – The Queen Alexandra's. After spending a year in Aldershot she was posted to Rinteln, in Germany.

Chester and Vivienne met at a party and she can remember thinking, 'This is it'. They went out for a year and got married in September 1979; a week later her twin sister married in Torbay. They stayed in

Germany for five years. Chester, who also belonged to the Royal Army Medical Corps, specialises in clinical measurements such as brain scans and ECGs.

Vivienne and Chester were always fit and healthy people. At school Vivienne was part of the All England Team for hurdling and sprinting. Getting married and having children was definitely part of her life plan, but it was only when it looked doubtful that she realised how important it was for her.

Cause of Infertility: Pelvic Inflammatory Disease.

Laura Edwards

Laura worked in advertising before leaving to start her own market research business. She deliberately became self-employed shortly after she married with the intention of building up some experience before she had a family.

Laura grew up in South Africa. She was the second child in her family. Her mother had married young and had her children early. This was not what she intended for her daughters though. Boyfriends were strictly disapproved of. Laura's sights were firmly set on academic achievement and a successful career. She more than fulfilled this expectation by going to university a year early, rapidly becoming a successful business woman and travelling abroad.

She arrived in Britain when she was twenty-five. It was at this time she met Robert and married him. Ironically, considering their later experience, he worked for ICI developing breeding techniques in farm animals. They met at Earl's Court Arena, where he was demonstrating pig insemination techniques.

Laura does not remember being overtly maternal as a young adult, but she always assumed she would have children. She is not someone who finds failure easy to deal with. Marriage and the thought of children brought out a different side of her personality which up until then she felt had been buried under a drive towards being 'successful'.

Cause of Infertility: Unremoved piece of an IUD (coil), endometriosis, low sperm count.

Rosemary Thornton

Rosemary trained as a teacher and worked in various schools in south London until she got married. She would describe herself as being entirely unambitious in the field of work. She became involved in a charismatic church in her twenties but is no longer part of any organised religion, although she still has a faith. She met and married David when she was thirty.

Rosemary was born to a single mother in 1950 and was adopted by a couple who could not have their own children. Rosemary's biological mother was living with one of their relatives. The adoption was arranged and a formal agreement drawn up. Her adopted mother's infertility was due to a series of miscarriages.

When Rosemary was nine or ten her adoptive mother showed her the official papers and a letter which was written to them by her father. These few pieces of evidence became very important to her as she was growing up and particularly at the time she was beginning to form an identity as an adult.

Rosemary always felt that when she had her own children she would fulfil a need in herself to have a genetically linked family. Both her own adoption and her need to have children of her own are very important issues in her life. She felt the circumstances of her birth left her with a feeling of rejection. She grew up with the idea that if she could bring a much-wanted child into the world, this might cancel out the pain she had experienced. Her experience of adoption also affected her decision not to adopt a child herself.

She went to an agency in London to ask them to help her search for her biological mother. The search took place over the same period as the events she describes in the following chapters.

Cause of infertility: Unknown; possibly due to an operation in her twenties.

Helen Pusey

Helen grew up in Kent and Sussex. She first came to London when she was nineteen. She took a cordon bleu cookery course and made a living cooking executive lunches for banks in the City and for private dinner parties, and eventually got a long-term job at a brewers. The working day was 10 am until 3 pm, and this fitted in very well with her intensive social life.

She met Jonathan because he also worked in the luxury food business. She was also involved in a charity called KIDS, which was set up by Lord Compton to help deprived children. Their social calendar included events such as Ascot, annual charity balls and large parties.

They married when Helen was twenty-nine and were both keen to try to have children fairly quickly. Helen's own childhood had not been particularly happy: she had been at boarding school from the age of eleven. The prospect of starting her own family was to her a way of wiping the slate clean and starting again. She wanted to give her children the close family life she had not experienced.

Cause of Infertility: Endometriosis.

CHAPTER 1

FINDING OUT ABOUT INFERTILITY

Many of us, with the help of effective contraception, spend our early reproductive years trying hard not to become pregnant. Fertility problems are only discovered when we do try to become pregnant. Although screening or early tests which might give an indication of fertility would be comforting for many women they are unlikely to be introduced by the National Health Service. They are low on any list of priorities for health care and their use is doubtful anyway since most doctors believe that pregnancy is the only sure test for fertility.

In this chapter, seven women explain how they came to know about their infertility problems and how they dealt with the news. Although there are many causes of infertility these women's experiences are among the most common. Few problems will show any obvious symptoms but sometimes, as in the case of endometriosis, there are symptoms which are apparent earlier in a woman's life.

Miranda Walsh is thirty-two and lives with her husband Clive in North London. She is a practising homeopath – a career she developed after university because she wanted a job which would be compatible with having children. They started to try to conceive in the late 1980s. At that time Clive was an NHS manager at the Hammersmith Hospital, where they eventually went for their treatment.

It was a gradual process of recognition and certainly it was me who knew first and had to convince everyone else. After a few months of trying I was very uneasy. I began to feel there was something wrong. Everyone else said things like, 'Oh well, it does take time,' or 'Maybe next month,' but by the summer of the year I had given up contraception I started to feel very unhappy. After eight or nine months of trying I went to see my GP; she was sympathetic but said it was quite natural for it to take a year. So I went on but there was an increasing uneasiness in me. It was a lonely time because no one else had any reason to think that there was a problem – it took Clive years and years to feel the same way I did about it.

The following January we started to have tests on my hormones, which didn't show anything, and Clive's sperm, which showed he was absolutely fine. The medical people I've come across have always been very sympathetic and helpful. I've never been dismissed or turned away. We knew the Hammersmith was a good centre and so we asked to be referred there. I still had a sense of hopelessness inside. People were continuing to say 'don't be so gloomy' or 'don't look on the black side – any minute now'.

By that time I had become interested in alternative medicine and was hoping that homeopathy might 'cure' me and that my fertility might be restored. So I did feel hopeful but somehow gloomy at the same time. I had a sense of barrenness and despair inside. I just felt that I was not fertile and that I couldn't have a baby. Every month comes by and it goes on and on in the same cycle.

I wanted to have all the tests. I knew I was going to the consultant to find out everything that I could. I wasn't afraid of the technology, in terms of finding out, but at that point I never dreamed I would have IVF or anything. I was still hoping and hoping that next month, before the appointment, I would be pregnant. All through the periods of tests I just hoped against hope that this was my lucky month and I would be able to say, 'Look, I don't need you, I did it on my own.' It's a kind of Chinese water torture – drip, drip, drip as the weeks go by.

I did find out what was wrong some months later. At the very first ultrasound scan, the doctor said to me, 'Oh, you've got polycystic ovaries, that's your problem'. I was taken aback because I didn't know about polycystic ovaries then. There were no signs early on. A lot of woman with polycystic ovaries are overweight and hairy and all kinds of things that mean they obviously aren't well, whereas I was always slim and there were never any physical symptoms. I've never been physically ill in any way. I'm very tuned in to my body and its cycles and there aren't any obvious signs of infertility – which is very hard to come to terms with. I can't even come to terms with it now.

There was a long period when I felt betrayed and alienated by my body. I would look at my belly and think what the hell's going on in there, why doesn't it work?

Polycystic ovaries are very common indeed. Many people with polycystic ovaries ovulate normally and are fully fertile. Nevertheless, polycystic ovary syndrome is one of the most common reasons for not ovulating. The ovaries develop many small follicles, which do not ovulate normally. It is thought to be due to an imbalance of the hormones of the ovaries. Other theories suggest that it is caused by an abnormality of the part of the brain which sends signals to the pituitary gland, which in turn sends hormonal messages to the ovaries to cause them to produce the mature eggs. If there is a malfunction of the pituitary gland this also results in an imbalance of hormones that are necessary for ovulation to happen effectively.

Polycystic ovaries are sometimes, as Miranda says, associated with other symptoms such as weight gain, a loss of periods and the growth of new hair (hirsutism). There are many other causes of failure to release an egg from the ovary, most of which are associated with a change in the periods or irregular menstration.

Liz Morris is thirty-six and lives in Hammersmith, London. She's a PR executive for an advertising company and the account she works on is a famous baby food manufacturer. Consequently she is 'surrounded by the little pink buggers'. She married Andy when she was twenty-seven. She had been married previously but had never attempted to have children. The gynaecology department at Charing Cross Hospital in London where she was seen no longer exists.

I had no idea I would have problems. My doctor put me on the pill originally because I had terrible acne and they used to put you on the pill as a hormonal treatment for that type of skin problem. So from the age of fourteen I just kept taking it and taking it and I never thought about infertility. At around the age of twenty-seven I came off the pill and found that I wasn't having any periods and it was around this time that I got together with my husband Andy. So from that time, although I did go back on the pill for a short time, until now at the age of thirty-six, I have not taken any precautions and I haven't become pregnant even once.

There is no evidence at all that taking the oral contraceptive pill causes infertility. Caroline's periods might have stopped whether she had been taking the pill or not.

I knew something needed investigating because my periods were so irregular. At first I attributed it to having been on the pill for so long. I thought my body was probably adjusting to not being on it any more. The doctor seemed to think the same. It was only after a year of odd shows of blood that I realized there was something more serious

11

wrong. I always hoped that getting pregnant would happen as a mistake, because the whole business of planning children was just weird. I wanted it to be a natural process.

We went away on holiday, took no precautions and just hoped it would happen. On the Sunday night when we returned home I received the news that my father had died and for the next year I felt so uptight, looking after my mother and things, that the idea of having children was really on the back burner.

Later on I decided I had better give up my job with the intention of really relaxing, because I was never going to get pregnant with my lifestyle. So then I trained as an aromatherapist – but that didn't pay the mortgage, so I went back to PR.

Eventually I got back to investigating the whole thing; I can remember the key moment when I found out something important. I was lying on a trolley in Charing Cross Hospital. It is a teaching hospital so there were three students and a gynaecology doctor. It was a rubber gloves job with legs akimbo and the gynaecologist started wittering at the students about my blood test results and testosterone and using incredibly long words about me. It wasn't just my medical condition it was me. I didn't mind the students being there because they have to learn, but I felt really excluded from the whole thing. I'd read a lot about it and was just about able to hang on to what he was saying and understand what was going on. But I was really pissed off and angry about it. At the end I said, 'Can you say that to me in English – what is happening to me?' And he said in a very blasé fashion, 'Oh, I think we can kick-start your system – get you ovulating again, I think there isn't a problem at all.' He used that expression 'kick-start' – it made me feel like a broken-down car. He didn't seem to have any idea that I might be anxious about the fact that I was not going to be able to have kids. The surprising thing was that he seemed to be quite young. I just expected him to have had some sort of training in these things.

Liz's sub-fertility was a minor hormonal imbalance. However it was later discovered that Andy also had a low sperm count, which would account for Liz's lack of success in getting pregnant. Many, if not most, cases of infertility are the result of two or more minor problems working together.

Sheila is forty. She teaches History in Scotland. She married when she was thirty. Before this she had not used contraception much because she had not been sexually active. The events she is describing took place from 1984.

I got married at thirty and a year after that I decided that I would try to have children. After about six months of trying and nothing happening I went to the doctor – really because other people suggested that I should. I thought the minute I tried to get pregnant I would. The doctor said come back in six months. Later I started going for investigations and I had a D and C (see below) which was inconclusive and they said, 'See if you get pregnant over the next six months.' After that I had a laparoscopy and that was when I found out that I had endometriosis. It hadn't even been suggested before this.

Now I feel anger about that time – angry at just how dismissive people can be. I feel now that it could have been investigated a lot earlier, in my twenties perhaps, and then something could have been done to sort it out.

Looking back I feel that I was a bit ignorant about these things; I should have known but I didn't. The signs were that sex was painful and that I was having very heavy periods. I have found out since that both of these symptoms are linked with endometriosis. My periods were usually excessively heavy and I remember from a very young age going to the doctors about menstrual problems – but no one took it very seriously. I also used to get very emotional around the time of my period but I never actually connected the two things till my period started.

I always assumed that I would have children, and I was very unaware of fertility problems. I knew that my aunt couldn't have children but it was never discussed in my family. A few years earlier I had worked with someone who had IVF and I was quite shocked. I had a very 'media' idea of it all – pioneering test-tube babies and that sort of thing – but I did feel sympathy.

Endometriosis is a reasonably common disease in which the endometrium – the lining of the womb – grows not only inside the uterus but also in the pelvic cavity, around the ovaries, the pelvic wall, the appendix, or even the bowel and the bladder. During the menstrual cycle this misplaced endometrium sheds blood, but unlike the endometrium in the uterus it has nowhere to go and builds up in the pelvic area, where it irritates the normal tissue and causes other problems such as cysts and scar tissue.

There is no evidence that endometriosis causes infertility except when the scarring is so bad that the tubes and ovaries are badly damaged by it. Many women with quite severe endometriosis do not have a fertility problem. Because the islands of endometrium depend on a woman's hormonal state, ironically, getting pregnant is one of the best treatments for endometriosis.

Before Sheila was diagnosed as having endometriosis she was taken into hospital for a D and C. Dilatation and Curettage is a womb scrape where the contents of the uterus are emptied by a surgical procedure. In his book Getting Pregnant, *Professor Robert Winston suggests that, 'Though harmless, it is valueless unless done at the time of a laparoscopy, when an endometrial biopsy is taken. It is performed because of a myth which suggests that it is easier to conceive after a D and C. There is no truth in this.'*

Vivienne Howard worked as a nanny before training as a nurse. After she joined the Queen Alexandra's she was posted to Germany where she met her husband Chester. She was twenty-seven when they married and was not intending to have children for another three or four years. She decided to change her method of contraception from the pill to a coil.

I'd been in Cyprus as a nanny and came back, and was probably about nineteen when I started my nursing training. We were given a very strong lecture about contraception when we went into nursing. A gynaecologist came in and said, 'Out of all of you in this room about five will end up getting pregnant.' There were about twenty of us. So we were very strongly advised to get some form of contraception. I was nineteen or twenty by then and that was the early Seventies and we all thought that it was better to be on the pill than to end up having a baby. It was a long span taking contraception and I was sexually active while I was training and before I was married.

We decided to get married in 1979. Because Chester is Jamaican, the question of children was there right from the beginning. The Padre asked us had we thought about our children being mixed race and the complications this might cause for them. I got married on 22 September and my twin sister got married on the 29th, so our married lives have really gone in tandem. This made it quite difficult later on when nothing was happening for us on the children front.

Once we were married I knew I didn't want to stay on the pill so I decided to have a coil fitted – it was a copper 7. Chester was very much against it, but he said it was up to me – he thought being on the pill for a long time was unlikely to be damaging. Up until that time I had no problems at all. I can't remember what made me decide to change – maybe in 1979 they were discussing the long-term effects of being on the pill or perhaps I was going through a health-kick stage. There must have been something in the newspapers, or maybe it was just me reaching twenty-seven or twenty-eight and thinking, 'I've been taking the pill for ten years, let's have a change.' I had the coil fitted in January.

Shortly after it was fitted I had a little bit of pain but not much and I went to see the doctor. He was very concerned because I had a mass (*swelling in her abdomen*). I went to the theatre in the hospital I worked at to have it investigated surgically and I had a laparoscopy. During the laparoscopy they blew gas into my abdomen so they would be able to see what was going on. It was painful, although I seem to have a high threshold for pain. I was frightened because I didn't know whether I would wake up with a little scar or having had major surgery. In the back of my mind there was the fear that the swelling was something malignant. I think, all the way along the line, the fact that there hasn't been a malignancy is how I've really come to terms with my infertility. Although it has been disastrous, I've always been able to think, 'It could have been a lot worse.'

It was diagnosed as hydrosalpinx (tubal blockage) and pelvic inflammatory disease. Obviously they removed the coil and told me that my fallopian tubes were damaged by infection and that my pelvis was also in a mess. Apart from the fact that I was in pain from the inflammation and swelling, I had to go on intravenous antibiotics which was also unpleasant. I then had to have three months of taking oral antibiotics to try and combat the infection and minimize the damage being caused.

Although it was minor surgery in terms of most gynaecological procedures, they kept me in for bed-rest for a week. I was off work for about a month. I don't think laparoscopies are always painful – it was made worse by the swelling and inflammation. I was on permanent painkillers.

At this point my husband was away but when he came back my consultant said we had to have another three months' abstinence. As you can imagine it was all very difficult for a newly married couple. It sounds awful, but afterwards we found it very difficult to get back to normal. So we basically just did nothing and I mean nothing. It was six months altogether and we both got used to switching off sexually because we had to. Eventually things did get back to normal but psychologically it was difficult to make the transition.

I think I must have been awful to live with, looking back on it, because I was in constant pain and discomfort. It affected my social life because I was tired all the time and things were quite difficult for a while – socially, sexually, everything really.

The doctor had laid it on the line about my fertility from the beginning. He said that he really wanted me to be aware that this was serious – that it wouldn't just mean taking tablets to get rid of it. There was always a bit of hope there, but he was always honest with us.

After six months of marriage with no sex, we were told to go away and definitely not use contraception because the consultant didn't think I should take the risk. This was still not our ideal time for starting a family but we just decided to go with what the doctor said. After a year or so with no pregnancy I had another laparoscopy with showed that both fallopian tubes were blocked.

Pelvic inflammatory disease, or PID, is a general term for an infection of the fallopian tubes and ovaries, often also involving adjacent tissue. If the fallopian tubes become swollen or inflamed the egg may not be able to pass into the uterus and so it will become difficult to conceive normally. PID can be a serious health problem, not only because of the immediate symptoms and complications which are often very painful, but even more so because of the long-term consequences – increased risk of ectopic pregnancy and infertility. An ectopic pregnancy is when a fertilized egg implants in the fallopian tube – at around six or seven weeks of pregnancy the growing foetus may burst the tube, which is potentially life threatening to the mother. It also has very severe consequences for her future fertility.

There is a growing body of evidence to show that young women, particularly those who have never been pregnant, are at risk of pelvic inflammatory disease through using the coil as a contraceptive device. The data is by no means clear and it has been difficult to pinpoint the coil as a single cause because many women using the coil also have had a number of different sexual partners, which would make them more at risk of PID anyway. However, it is now fairly common practice only to insert the coil in women who have already had a child.

PID affects fertility because even after the infection has cleared up, adhesions and scar tissue can still cause blockages. The infection can also damage the cells which live in the fallopian tubes. This prevents them from efficiently guiding the egg from the ovary down the fallopian tube. For pregnancy, the egg must be transferred into the uterus down the fallopian tube. The fallopian tubes are attached to the ovaries and the fimbria, at the end of the tube, can move around the ovary to pick up the egg and guide it down the tube to the uterus. When PID has caused much damage, the fimbriac end of the tube is immobilized by scar tissue,which decreases the ability of the end of the tube to pick up eggs.

L aura Edwards is from South Africa originally but now works in London as a freelance marketing consultant. She and Robert got married in 1986 when she was twenty-six and he was twenty-eight. Robert also ran his own business. They decided to try to have children straightaway.

It wasn't that I'd always wanted to have children, but it wasn't that I had ever not wanted to have children. Having children was something I had always assumed was going to just happen. I think that's what a lot of people think. All your sexual life you struggle with contraception. You just think that when you stop contraception, you'll conceive.

After we got married, we already had a house and a good set-up so naturally we thought about having children. After about four months I went and had my IUD (coil) removed. The string came off the IUD but no IUD emerged. I was sent to the Chelsea Women's Hospital to have the IUD removed by D and C. They managed to get some of it out. It was originally a T-shaped IUD, but the piece that came out was L-shaped, missing the other cross bar of the T. When I came round from the anaesthetic they said they had got most of it out and what was left shouldn't cause a problem. I was left knowing I had this little bit of the IUD left in, and wondering whether this was a barrier to conception or not.

I wasn't aware of the problems some women have when using an IUD. The coil was fitted in South Africa, and I have never since heard of a coil having a string break off. It occurred to me that I should find out who manufactures the coil and damn well sue them. It wasn't as if it had been in there for fifteen years without any attention. It was fitted only two years before.

I went on the pill when I was eighteen. I didn't really like the idea of pumping hormones into my body, which is ironic when I consider all the treatment I have had since. I attributed being slightly overweight to the pill. The coil stopped you getting pregnant when it was there and you didn't have to remember to take it, so that's what I liked about the coil. I had three over the years. I never had any problems with the first two coils.

At the hospital I remember there was a girl lying in the bed beside me, who must have been about eighteen. The doctors came in and pulled the screens around her. They said this was the third time they had seen her in there that year, and were warning her that abortion was not a form of contraception and that she really had to do something about it. She said that she would wait to see what her boyfriend said. They said they wouldn't wait for her boyfriend.

17

Here was someone who took absolutely no care and she did get pregnant just like that. It was unusual that I was listening to this conversation. She was eighteen and had been pregnant three times. She seemed to see termination as a more logical form of contraception than doing anything else about it. The doctors were obviously terribly irritated.

I can remember thinking that I'd end up just like her, now that I had the IUD out.

Rosemary is forty-four and lives with her husband in Shirley, South London. At present she doesn't work, but she trained as a teacher. She herself was adopted shortly after her birth by a couple who could not have children. However, her own adoption caused a deep crisis for her about her identity; she felt having her own children would create the genetically linked family she had always craved. But she also felt she could not go through the process of adopting a child having experienced it herself.

I think when you're a child everything is simplistic. You form beliefs and you take them into your subconscious and you think well this is the situation and this will resolve it. And from a fairly young age I used to think, 'When I marry and I have my own children, then I will know where I belong, then I will know who the real me is.' I can't say when I started to believe that, I just know I did believe it. A lot of adopted people feel it will be resolved maybe if they meet their mother; I don't think that was necessarily at the forefront of my mind. My feelings were that I would find myself when I eventually had my own children.

It didn't occur to me that anything would go wrong; I had an idealized picture of having three children and of a fulfilled life beginning. The beginning of finding me. We married when I was thirty and I was so happy and I had no reason to believe that things wouldn't continue like that.

My adoptive mother had trouble conceiving and had several miscarriages. Yet I never imagined anything like that happening to me. I don't think it occurred to me. Maybe the fact that she wasn't physically my mother – perhaps at the back of my mind I felt because I hadn't got a blood tie or a genetic tie the things that went wrong for her wouldn't go wrong for me.

We tried to conceive for a few months and I started to worry that I wasn't pregnant. It was quite naive of me. I've since realized that even fertile couples can take a year or more. But I wasn't aware of any of that, it just wasn't an area that I knew very much about. I just thought that we would try for a baby and it would happen.

I went to see a GP who I knew was really sympathetic and someone I could talk to in Streatham. I told him we'd been trying for some months and he said, 'Well it isn't really very long but in view of your age' – because I was then thirty-four – 'I'll refer you to Kings College Hospital,' and I got an appointment fairly quickly.

At first they asked us questions about our background and our lives and took blood tests. David had to give sperm to be analysed and although he had some sort of infection they treated it with antibiotics and afterwards did more tests and he was absolutely fine. They asked about my medical history, what sort of operations I'd had. I started to get a little bit suspicious when I told them about the operation I'd had in my late twenties – a presacral neurectomy. The doctor seemed quite surprised that I'd had such major surgery and he asked me why. I could see by the look on his face that he thought it might have serious consequences. Eventually he suggested that they do a laparoscopy to have a good look inside and to see the condition of my tubes.

I can remember lying in bed in hospital one Saturday evening and the doctor came to see me and said he'd got the results of the laparoscopy. In his opinion there was no chance whatsoever of my ever having children. I was absolutely desolate. I just couldn't believe it but he was quite positive about it. He was quite firm and he asked if I understood, and I said, 'Yes, I understand,' and he probably went on to say other things. I don't remember any more of the conversation. He said, 'I'm sorry' and he just went.

Because he'd been so positive that there wasn't any chance I almost accepted it. I thought well it's so final there's nothing I can do about it. I was in absolute despair but I did accept it.

Helen is a trained cordon bleu cook and used to cook executive lunches for the Courage Brewery. She met Jonathan, who had a business supplying luxury fish to restaurants in London, when she was twenty-eight. She lived in Chelsea and remembers that period of her life as great fun – endless socializing at charity balls. She and Jonathan married when she was twenty-nine.

I think the first inkling that I had about possible infertility was in my early twenties. I had cervical cancer. When that was diagnosed and treated endometriosis was also discovered. I went to the gynaecologist because I was having persistent pelvic pain. I thought it might be something to do with having had my appendix out, but he suggested I have a smear test and it came back as abnormal. Nowadays they do laser treatment but I was treated with liquid nitrogen. (*The liquid nitrogen is used to freeze tissue which later dies and falls off. The process is called cryo cautery and has now been replaced by laser treatment.*)

The treatment itself was not particularly humiliating but afterwards I had to have a colposcopy (internal examination of the cervix). The consultant was followed into the room by a group of students – all male and all about the same age as me. He never asked me if I minded and when I was obviously agitated he said, 'Don't fuss. This is not the *Tatler*. You're not in *Homes and Gardens* now.' I just wanted some privacy. I've never forgotten it. It was such a put-down. After the treatment there was a long period when I had to use sanitary towels because I had a horrible discharge.

I asked questions about what implications there might be for my ability to have children but the doctors were really quite evasive. I think because, as they pointed out to me, I didn't have a boyfriend at the time let alone being married and trying to have children. But I wanted to know. They said the treatment – the cryo cautery – shouldn't in itself create a problem. But they were concerned about the endometriosis. They decided at that stage, in 1979, that because I wouldn't be imminently trying to have children, it wasn't necessary to treat it and they left it.

From then on it was always at the back of my mind. I had regular periods, so I knew that I was ovulating, but I had a long cycle and the menstruation time was often painful. I never knew for sure if there would be a problem because they never ran any tests to see if I was infertile. I don't think there is a test except getting pregnant.

I've always found with doctors, all the way through, that they offer you a little information at a time. They wait to see how you take that on board and react. They don't tell you everything straightaway. They wait for you to ask the questions – if you don't ask the questions they assume that you aren't ready to hear that piece of information yet so they don't tell you more. I don't really agree with them doing that. I was originally told that a few cells had been cancerous. It wasn't until I read the BUPA insurance report that I realized it was fairly serious and that was apparently a 'toned-down version'.

Before I met Jonathan I had a couple of other quite serious boyfriends. I felt it was important to tell them early on that I might have problems with conceiving children. It was purely selfish because I didn't want them or me to become attached if it was going to put them off. I know it made a difference. I know that they very much wanted marriage and children and didn't want to start off with any of the odds against them achieving that. I always felt that I would have children but I was aware that it wasn't going to be straightforward. I was prepared for it to take longer than normal.

It was completely different meeting Jonathan. I definitely had that feeling that this was going to be the one. I somehow knew that it wasn't going to be a problem to him because he wasn't that kind of person. I think anyone who had cared that much would have turned out to be a very shallow person. He said we would just cross that bridge when we came to it. I think we both thought I might have to have a bit of help but neither of us was imagining anything as invasive as GIFT.

I remember reading about Louise Brown's birth (*the first test-tube baby, born in 1978*) – and thinking how miraculous it was. I was also aware of the ethical implications for later on – medical discoveries never remain static, they always lead on to other developments and I found that side of it worrying. Later on, when I knew more about endometriosis and was aware of my own problems, I took more of a personal interest. Until I actually met Jonathan and started to think of children as a real possibility it all seemed like a very distant issue in the media.

We started to try for children more or less immediately, but the first year it was a fairly vague attempt. It was the following year that it became obvious there was a problem. The first time I went to see my gynaecologist he wasn't unduly worried and told me to come back in six months. I went back and said that I was aware of my cycle and that nothing was happening even when we tried at the appropriate time. He said he thought he should do a laparoscopy.

Infertility

Over the last fifteen years, the trauma of infertility has received an enormous amount of attention. In vitro fertilization has gone from being a rare and miraculous medical event to a fairly routine treatment. But is this just an increase in public awareness or are there reasons to believe that infertility is becoming an increasing problem?

What does it mean?

The medical profession would regard a couple as having 'decreased fertility' if they have not achieved a pregnancy within twelve months of trying to have unprotected sex at the appropriate time of the month (ie when the woman is ovulating). The variation in how quickly couples who are fertile conceive is enormous – very fertile couples may achieve pregnancy within one or two months whereas others can take up to twelve or more cycles. Not enough is really known about the biological differences between couples who appear to be very fertile and those who take much longer to conceive. Many more studies need to be carried out looking at couples who are fertile in order to reveal the answers to the problems of infertility.

How common is it?

From the studies which have been carried out in Europe and America it would appear that 15 per cent of all couples experience infertility at some point during their reproductive years. Some of that 15 per cent are people who have difficulty having already had one child; this is called secondary infertility. About 7.5 per cent of couples will not succeed in having the number of children they wished for.

Has there been an increase in recent years?

The answer to this question is complicated; the huge increase in public awareness, particularly since the birth of the first test-tube baby, Louise Brown, in 1978, has brought with it an increase in the number of people attending infertility clinics. One might assume from this that infertility is an increasing problem or that the same infertility problems were there before – but because there were no treatments couples didn't bother going to the doctor and therefore were never diagnosed.

To compare the present with the past is difficult because the methods of categorization and measurement are often different. Textbooks on gynaecology and obstetrics published in the Fifties and early Sixties stated that at the time, 7-8 per cent of newly weds experienced infertility as a problem. Today's equivalent figures are between 15 and 20 per cent. (W. Feichtinger, 'Environmental factors and fertility', *Human Reproduction* vol. 6, (1991) 1170-1175). This comparison does not prove much because there are many other factors which may have caused variations. Statistically it is not really possible to prove an increase.

Studies carried out to try to support the hypothesis that there has been an increase in infertility have looked at possible biological and cultural factors. Diseases which often used to be the cause of infertility, such as gonorrhoea and tuberculosis, are more treatable today. Infertility due to chlamydia or particular types of environmental pollution may be increasing, though it may simply be that (moderately) reliable tests have only recently been developed.

Are sperm counts falling?

In 1992 the *British Medical Journal* published a report about a fall in the average male sperm count which started a huge debate about whether the Western male could become sterile in the next century. The original survey by Danish researchers rang alarm bells worldwide and possible explanations became more and more exaggerated. One fear was that widespread use of the contraceptive pill might be causing oestrogen pollution in water and affecting male fertility. There were also theories about increased stress levels and tighter clothing in the 1960s reducing the ability of men's testicles to produce adequate sperm.

In Spring 1994, after many column inches and several hours of television had been devoted to the implications of this drop in the sperm count, Professor Ian Stewart, from the University of Warwick, reanalysed the original data. He has shown that what was thought to be a huge drop in the sperm count can be explained by a methodological mistake. 'There is no evidence from these data for a significant decline in sperm number. If there is any decline it is far, far smaller than was claimed.' The original report said sperm density had nearly halved and semen quality had decreased by nearly 25 per cent since 1940.

The new analysis does not disprove the theory that there has been a decline but it does seriously undermine what was thought to be strong statistical evidence. Other researchers in reproductive biology have said that there is still reason to believe that there has been a decline in male fertility. 'Sperm-count figures are very difficult to study, but we can no longer find men with high sperm counts. Where have they gone? What's more important is the rise in testicular cancer, the increase in the number of babies born with undescended testes and the increase in congenital abnormalities of the male foetus.' (Professor Dennis Lincoln, the Medical Research Council Reproductive Biology Unit, quoted in the *Daily Telegraph*, 12 April 1994: 'Fear of Male Infertility is Unfounded' by Christine McGourty, Technology Correspondent.)

Has female infertility increased?

One of the most important cultural changes has been the age at which women choose to have their children. In Western countries there are several reasons why couples choose to wait: women wanting to establish themselves in careers before having children, couples deciding to wait until they become financially secure and many people now feel that they will make a better parent and choice of partner with the maturity that age brings.

In 1990 women were between two and three years older when they delivered their first child than in 1970. A woman's age has been shown to be a significant factor in conception. Women's fecundity (ability to conceive children) starts to decrease as early as between the ages of twenty-two and twenty-five, and after they are thirty-five infertility increases. There are now significantly more women who never have children – a study in Denmark showed that 17 per cent of women in the financial sector had no children at the age of thirty-five.

One of the most significant reasons why we wait to have our

children is because we can now use effective contraception to plan our families. Many women have worried about using contraception and the possible consequences the pill or coil may have on their fertility later on. In the next chapter women describe how they felt about their previous use of contraceptives and at the end of the chapter there is a brief description of the medical literature concerning contraception and fertility.

CHAPTER 2

LOOKING FOR REASONS

For many women the initial shock that they may not be able to have children is followed by a long struggle to accept the bad news. The stigma which surrounds infertility often creates a feeling that they themselves are to blame for the problem. Some women spend years ruminating over the past and looking for explanations about what they did wrong. In nearly all cases there is no evidence to suggest that they caused their own infertility. Miranda, Liz, Sheila, Vivienne, Laura and Rosemary now explain how they eventually came to rationalize these fears.

Miranda was still waiting to hear what the specific cause of her and her husband's failure to conceive might be. By this time she was sure that there was a problem but others around her were not yet convinced. She was beginning to feel that this difference of opinion was creating a barrier with those she was close to and making her feel very lonely.

I'd been through endless ruminations: I did something wrong; it was because I was on the pill; it was because of this or because of that. Then lots of people suggested to me subtly or not so subtly that it was something to do with my personality. If only I'd relax, get my exams out of the way. One person actually suggested to me that I set my standards too high. At the time I was training to be a homeopath and they thought that my infertility was a temporary problem caused by me being too interested in good grades in my exams. That was such a load of crap.

I did feel at the time that being on the pill might have caused the problem. I felt that it was common sense that if you tamper with your body's hormones for a period of five years, as I had, it is possible that they might not work properly afterwards.

The consultant said there is no evidence of this. I was either born this way or the cause is unknown. I came to terms with this guilt over a period – I thought back to the time I was on the pill from when I was sixteen to when I was twenty-one. I thought, 'Who's to say that an unplanned pregnancy wouldn't have been a disaster in my life?' I was at university and I just wasn't ready then, so how could I go back and condemn my sixteen-year-old self who didn't know any better. Everyone was on the pill. I now think there was nothing wrong with the decision I made at the time.

I do have a tendency to blame myself anyway – I'm hard on myself. I got angry and upset by thinking somehow I didn't deserve a baby. I took on these ideas that it was because I was so keen to do well in exams. The implication seemed to be that I was emotionally frigid. No one suggested that I was actually sexually frigid, but it all went together in a package really.

Everyone clings to this idea that if you relax you'll fall pregnant naturally. It goes along the lines of 'If you give up your job and stop worrying about it it will happen.' 'Have you thought about adopting? – I knew someone who adopted and then got pregnant naturally.' It becomes ridiculous, they say, 'I know someone who got two dogs and then had a baby.' The idea is that you are preventing yourself from getting pregnant by being uptight; if only you can somehow be distracted nature will reassert itself. Now I think this is all a load of rubbish – but it was one of the most painful parts of the process of being infertile. I felt I was being accused of creating the problem myself.

I felt so strongly about it all that I did my thesis for homeopathy on psychological causes of infertility in my final year – and it vindicated what I had originally thought. I worked on it for months and interviewed lots of people and thought about it very hard. And I think that was my way of dealing with all those psychological pressures which people were putting on me and all of those suggestions.

I realized that when you read some research that states 35 per cent of women who were on a mind and body relaxation programme did conceive when they hadn't been able to before it meant that 65 per cent of the women didn't conceive. So for some women there may be emotional factors but it's by no means universal.

A Mind Body programme for infertility was carried out in an American Hospital and the results were written up in an article which appeared in Fertility and Sterility *in February 1990. The first 54 women to complete a behavioural treatment programme based on the elicitation of the relaxation response showed statistically significant decreases in anxiety, depression and fatigue as well as increases in vigour. In addition, 34 per cent of these women became pregnant within six months of completing the programme. (Domar, Seibel, Benson, 'The Mind Body Program for infertility: a new behavioural treatment for women with infertility.' Fertility and Sterility, 53: 2, (February 1990).) As Miranda points out, this also means that 66 per cent of the women did not become pregnant. The problem with this study is that approximately one-third of women will conceive within one year, without any specific treatment, if there is no clear-cut cause of infertility. The suggested conclusion here, that relaxation may help in infertility, is not proved. Behavioural therapy may, however, help in coping with infertility.*

There were other things which did not make sense and completely refuted this idea that you could control your reproductive capabilities. It was at the time when the international press was revealing the atrocity of Bosnian women becoming pregnant after being raped. I thought about how much those women must have been psychologically disturbed. Your emotions may sometimes connect directly with your fertility but not always. And those women, who didn't want to be pregnant, certainly hadn't willed their pregnancies and a lot of them wanted to be rid of them.

I came to the idea in the end that having children is a blind evolutionary force – and that was partly why it was so painful not to be able to have them because it was such a deep-seated need in me to have them. But also, it was out of my control because it was like evolution – a completely uncontrollable force. And that you could only tamper with it to a certain extent. You could be raped and the most miserable in the world and yet conceive because it was separate from you somehow.

For me this lifted a huge burden – I began to realize that I was uptight and unhappy because I was infertile not the other way round.

Miranda looked at both conventional and alternative treatments for infertility. There is a difficulty in trying to compare homeopathic treatments with other treatments because the evidence is largely anecdotal. Most medical techniques and drugs would be tested in double blind placebo trials. Homeopaths believe their therapies are about individualizing and that homeopathy does not lend itself easily to this type of evaluation.

Miranda found a large number of cases which were cured after the patient had received homeopathic remedies. 'These cases can be seen individually as being merely anecdotal and of not proving anything in themselves, but as a body of evidence they are more persuasive.'' She also points out that 'sometimes homeopathy may offer broader success in achieving other health goals with the patient even if their fertility is not restored.'

Liz and Andy had been together long enough for other people to ask them why they didn't have any children yet. Liz continued to hope that a pregnancy would happen naturally. Neither of them showed any symptoms of illness. If anything they were very fit.

Everyone tells you that it is because you are not relaxing. I went to a family wedding and Auntie Rini, who has three children, told me, 'Oh don't worry about it luv, I know plenty of people who, as soon as they decided they didn't want to have children, got pregnant.' I have heard this over and over again. It is no help and I don't believe it. It is not to do with unwinding and destressing – that probably has a minuscule part to play. Even though I have a fairly stressed job I also know that both Andy and I have physiological reasons for our lack of conception. I refuse to blame my job or my lifestyle. I know that is completely irrelevant.

What I did blame myself for was that I had taken the pill for so long – from the time I was 14 until I was 29. I remember thinking, 'Oh my God, it's my own fault – I've buggered up my system with chemicals.' So I did blame myself for allowing myself to be on the pill for so long. But then I know loads of other women who have taken it and they haven't had any problems.

> *The pill has been thought by many to be a cause of infertility. There is no scientific evidence to support this suggestion. Studies by the Royal College of General Practitioners in Britain show that 80 per cent of all women who have never had a baby and 90 per cent of those who have, will have conceived within one year of stopping the pill. This is exactly the same proportion of pregnancies found in women who have not used contraception previously. The length of time a woman is on the pill is not significant either.*

Sheila had been told that her lack of success in becoming pregnant was probably due to endometriosis. The cells which create the endometrium, the lining of the womb, sometimes gather in other areas of the abdomen and when they bleed during the period of menstruation they can create blockages which prevent normal ovulation. Because of this Sheila felt she carried the burden of responsibility for her failure to conceive. At this point in the treatment her husband's sperm count had still not been tested.

I don't think it registered immediately, but I think that as the years went on, I began to feel at some level that I had caused the endometriosis. I became convinced that something like endometriosis has a psychological cause. The fact that I denied my sexuality all through my twenties makes me look back and think it must be linked. I don't think I've ever had a very good body image. I just have a really strong feeling that there is a connection between body image and infertility. The idea that I was storing up repressed emotions seemed to fit with the idea that I had these pockets of stored up, misplaced tissue. I just don't think these things happen by chance. I went through feeling that I had failed.

It must have been a good two years into my treatment before they investigated my husband. I had already shouldered a lot of the responsibility and then it was found that he had a low sperm count and he would have to have the 'cold water' treatment.

It was around this time I started taking responsibility for my own body. I thought it was important to take much more care of myself and what I ate. I was working with someone who was an alternative therapist so I started seeing her on a professional basis and changing my diet. She recommended this Foresight Organization which is an organization concerned with pre-conceptual care.

I went for all kinds of tests to find what I was allergic to. I took all this quite seriously, but my husband didn't or wouldn't. I ended up feeling really, really angry with him, because I was putting myself through all these different things and he really wasn't doing anything. For instance I wanted to stop drinking, and I wanted to change our diet and lifestyle. This caused a lot of stress on my part, and resentment, because I'd be giving him the cold water treatment every morning and he used to get really annoyed with me. It was a really horrible experience.

Some doctors recommend that men with low sperm counts wear loose boxer shorts and bathe the scrotum daily in very cold water. The idea is that reducing the testicular temperature will improve sperm production. There is no real proof that this works and as Sheila describes it can come to be seen as a form of torture.

I suppose I wanted some element of control and I felt that my lifestyle had become quite unhealthy as well.

Not long after this, when I had just started some infertility treatment

I remember going to my doctor because they weren't sure if I should continue the treatment. So I asked my GP if he could recommend me for IVF, and he actually said to me, 'as far as I'm concerned, people with hip replacements are of far more concern than you. Which would you rather, not being able to walk or not being able to have a child?' I was absolutely stunned! I was in a state of shock and was hardly able to walk out of the surgery. It was a really punitive thing to say to me. It was horrible. I just couldn't believe it. I never went back to him, needless to say.

The link in many people's minds between infertility and stress is due to the fact that many women, at some time during their lives, have a month or two when they don't ovulate. It is often at times of great stress – moving house, the death of a parent, losing a job, marital breakdown or if they are suffering from depression. Some women are more sensitive to stress than others. Infertility experts think that it is rare that stress is the cause of a persistent failure to ovulate. It is unlikely, too, that many of the other causes of infertility are due to psychological causes. There is no evidence of a link between endometriosis and repressed sexuality. Being healthy and having plenty of exercise is obviously a good thing in itself.

Vivienne also considered the possibility that it was her own fault when she was diagnosed with pelvic inflammatory disease. As a nurse she was aware of the risks of infection from the coil and also aware that pelvic inflammatory disease may be linked to sexually transmitted diseases.

On hearing this news about the pelvic inflammatory disease I was very open with the consultant and I said to him, 'Is it just because of the coil or is it perhaps because I wasn't a good girl before I got married? If there is anything nasty kicking about, if I had a venereal disease or anything my husband and I are both open enough in our relationship to cope with that kind of possibility.' But he said no – he thought it might have been the fact that the coil was fitted. They would never actually say that it was an infection from the coil. It was strange that everything had been OK up until then, and three months after that was fitted was the only time that I had any gynaecological problems whatsoever.

I think from the first mention of pelvic inflammatory disease I had been worrying in the back of my mind that I or Chester might have been responsible in some way. The consultant said that because I had never had any discharge or problems before it was likely to have been a previous infection. He could never say categorically 'it was the coil' because then I would have been in a position to ask what they were going to do about it.

It was about five or six years afterwards that the coil was withdrawn as a contraceptive device for women who had not had children because so many people were having problems with their fertility. But I now completely accept that it was my decision to use that form of contraception for whatever reason; nobody said 'OK, this is what you must do.'

But you look back and you think 'what if I had done things differently? Would the outcome have been any different?' That's where the guilt thing comes in. I had a long span of contraception and I was sexually active while I was training to be a nurse and before I was married. I have thought about that time many times when I have been very low.

The effect of the news was absolutely devastating. I went from being an amazingly confident, sociable, open person to a feeling of deep, deep failure – failure as a woman, failure as a wife, failure as a person. I took it so badly. I just started looking back to the time before I got married and thought if only I'd done things differently.

Laura was always convinced that she would conceive eventually. Having decided it was the right time to start trying she was keen to become pregnant as soon as possible. She felt her problems were caused by the piece of coil which had broken off during the operation to remove it.

I didn't really feel it was my fault. All the time that they were messing about with the coil I was really frustrated that nothing was being done quickly. At the same time I was thinking that the way an IUD works is to create a barrier inside the uterus and I still have a third of the barrier left. Is it only when it's three thirds there that it works and when you take two thirds out is it definitely not going to work? Also I've heard of babies being born holding an IUD.

After another eight months or so, and no pregnancy, we were referred to a specialist who said as far as he was concerned, as long as I had an obstruction in my uterus (one third of an IUD constituted an obstruction) then I would be unlikely to get pregnant and he would not be happy to consider me as a low fertility problem until that had been removed. Then we'd have to wait another eight months to a year to try.

I thought, 'Great, I'll be an old woman by the time this is all sorted.' He suggested that I have a D and C and if that didn't work he would do something else. He wanted to get the piece out, because until that happened we couldn't say I had a fertility problem.

I was still with the NHS. They got my IUD out and they also told me that I had some endometriosis, and that one of my tubes looked slightly blocked. However during the lap and dye procedure they had blown fluid through the tube to unblock it. After that I thought that I was theoretically OK, but I was now learning about endometriosis which I hadn't even heard of before. I was also coming to terms with the fact that one of my tubes was slightly dodgy. But my memory of my overall feeling at that time is that we believed we had the problem sorted. However the specialist told me that as the IUD was now out he wanted to try and clear up the endometriosis. The best thing they can do is to put you on drugs that completely suppress all ovulation (Danazol), so you have no oestrogen for six months.

The principle behind drug treatments for endometriosis is to reduce the amount of oestrogen in the woman's body, which in turn reduces the ability of the lining of the uterus to grow. This causes the deposits of endometrium outside the uterus to stop spreading and perhaps shrink. Danazol which is a vaguely similar compound to testosterone would have a similar effect. Women who experience a lot of pain from endometriosis find it is relieved by suspending their cycle for some months. Many women seem to feel unwell when receiving the drug, and some have unpleasant side-effects such as bloating, headaches and spots on the face.

The best treatment for endometriosis is pregnancy but I was unlikely to get pregnant. The doctors didn't have an explanation for what caused it. I joined the Endometriosis Society and learned a little bit about it. The hormones made me feel as if I was on the pill continually. It meant I didn't ovulate, didn't have any periods, and put on weight. I did not like being on Danazol at all. I was meant to be on it for six to eight months. After three months I just said I didn't like it. I had skipped three periods and felt I wanted to get on with getting pregnant. I went back and said I was really not happy about the drug, and thought if the endometriosis was only minor why put me on it for eight months. I really wanted to get off it. I was feeling big and unwell. The specialist agreed.

At that point I was thinking it's all very well for male doctors who may have teenaged children, but a year is made up of twelve calendar months, and to put you on Danazol for eight months is like saying let's put off your possibility of having children for another year. I had already wasted a lot of time with this ridiculous removal of the IUD that went wrong, and then eight months later going in again for the other half. Why didn't they just do it all at the same time? You just see the years being wasted.

During Rosemary's early twenties several emotional and physical problems combined to create a crisis in her life. It was in 1979 that she decided to try and seek help. She went to see a consultant who felt that if he could treat her severe period pains her psychological problems might also be eased. He performed an operation on her called a presacral neurectomy.

Later on, after she married and received the doctor's depressing news about her chances of having a baby, Rosemary started to think back to that earlier time to find reasons for her infertility.

I became increasingly depressed in my late twenties, not really knowing why I was not able to make relationships work. The confusion was unbearable. I wanted to get married and have children, largely because I saw it as my way of coming to terms with my identity problem. But I also didn't want to commit myself. I think I hurt people by running away.

I would get up feeling really tearful. I was teaching and had to make myself get to work. Then I would try and put on a bright face whilst at work but as soon as work was finished I'd come home and just not want to do anything and feel very depressed. Eventually I did get help and had therapy.

Physically, I was having more and more problems with severe pain during periods. I would be in bed for a couple of days a month. My periods were really heavy and the pain was absolutely unbearable, sometimes I would just have to crawl along the floor. I couldn't get any relief from the pain. Even if I went to bed and had a hot water bottle and painkillers it was dreadful.

The doctor had given me tablets but they didn't help at all. I think the physical and mental problems merged into each other. I found that one month was rolling into another; that I'd just be getting on my feet again after a period, then it would almost be time for another. So the times when I was feeling well were becoming less and less. I think, looking back, that obviously had an effect on my mental health. It was a time in my life when things reached a crisis point. This whole thing of identity became almost obsessional. I became increasingly less in touch with myself and people around me.

I did have therapy at that time and it helped enormously. I hadn't consciously verbalized the things that I'd felt at school and earlier in my life. I'd never actually given them words, I knew it was all there and that I had all these feelings but it was all a muddle. Until then I hadn't actually sat down and talked about my past life to anyone. I mean you just live, you get on with it. I'd never analysed it. Actually sitting down with someone who asked me about my childhood and school life, all these things started to surface. I began to realize how greatly being adopted had influenced me and was in some ways holding me back from being able to form good relationships and a commitment.

My periods had been a problem from the beginning. I first went into hospital for a D and C when I was about eighteen because I was bleeding in between periods. In my twenties the pain got worse and it really began to affect my life. I began to take time off every month. Although the headmistress I had at the time was really kind and understanding, she did take me aside one day and say, 'Look can you see if you can do something about it because it is causing us a few problems.'

I had heard of someone in Harley Street through a friend of a friend. They said he was quite good. It wasn't the sort of place that somebody like me went to really, it was a bit daunting. By that time I was just so desperate, and I thought that if I could sort out the physical side of my problems other things might start to improve.

When I first went to the private gynaecologist he suggested tablets and I tried quite a few different kinds and strengths. None of them really worked. Eventually he said to me, 'Well there is an operation that I can perform. It's called a presacral neurectomy.' I'd never heard of that and I didn't really take in the details of what he would actually do but he said it had something to do with the nerves in the womb and it would stop the pain because there wouldn't be any sort of sensation or feeling. I can remember saying, 'It sounds a bit drastic, will there be any sort of side-effects in the future?' I meant problems with fertility or anything like that and I can remember him saying, 'absolutely none, no problems whatsoever'. He was quite categorical – it wasn't that I didn't understand.

So I went away to think about it for a while. I had another dreadful month of horrendous pain and thought right I'll go for it. I don't think even at that point I'd realized it would be a major operation which was stupid of me. I think because up until then I'd just had D and Cs and things, I felt it would be like that. I don't think I'd taken on board that I'd have to be cut or anything.

I started to realise what a major operation it had been when I woke to find this wound across my abdomen. I think I was told at the time I had about thirty stitches inside. I was in a ward with a lady who had a hysterectomy and she went home a long time before me. I was in for about two weeks. So then I knew it was pretty serious stuff.

When the decision was made I didn't feel at ease. I was intimidated by the private rooms in Harley Street. He was the top surgeon in the country. I completely put my trust in him and I didn't ask very much. If he said that this would work and that there would be no side effects afterwards, I believed it completely.

I haven't ever had any pain with a period from that time so it did work. I think many women will think that I was really stupid. I think that about myself now, looking back. He said it wouldn't affect my future fertility and I took him at his word really, which I've since learnt was a daft thing to do.

He was extremely smart – 'dapper' I think would be the word. He always looked very elegant, very expensive suits, expensive shirts and ties, absolutely immaculate and his hands and nails were perfect. His whole air, his whole appearance, was just one of everything being in its place. Although he was quite a strange person, I accepted his behaviour as being part of his place and position. I thought this was how people in Harley Street were. He'd often say things to me like, 'I'm a very clever doctor you know' – almost childish really. But because I was in a world that I felt was alien anyway, I accepted anyone's behaviour as being a normal part of that world.

Looking back I've questioned his ethics about doing the operation at all and the things he told me about it. There was an incident the last time I came to see him that made me doubt other things that he had told me. I had to come and see him quite a few times after the operation for checkups. I always went in on my own, he didn't have a nurse or anyone in the rooms either. He was on his side of the desk and I was sitting on a chair on the other side. He got a key from his pocket and undid a drawer and he took out some photographs, gave them to me and said, 'You might like to look at these.' In all innocence I started shuffling through the photographs and they were pornographic photographs of sexual acts – oral sex and things that I found absolutely horrifying and frightening. I didn't know how to react and I couldn't believe it, I just couldn't believe it.

I think he got quite a bit of pleasure from seeing how ill at ease and nervous I was and he actually said to me, 'You can see what they are and you can see what they're doing. There are lots of people who do that sort of thing.' I don't think I acknowledged it at all, I just put them on the table. I can't remember much about what happened after that because I was in such a state, I just could not believe that this had happened. I was frightened and shocked. It seemed incredible that someone in his position would do that. Afterwards I think there was almost a feeling of did I imagine that because it was so awful. I hadn't seen photographs like that before in my life. I came out and I burst in to tears and I just said I don't want to come back any more and I didn't ever come back.

Now I feel very, very angry that I didn't do something about it but I still don't know what I could have done. He was a Harley Street surgeon at the top of his profession, and he had a good reputation. It would have been his word against mine because there were just the two of us in the consulting room. At the end of the day he could have just denied the whole thing; I hadn't got any proof.

I can remember thinking he wouldn't have behaved like that to the other patients that I'd seen because they were obviously older and they looked pretty assertive sort of people and wealthy. I felt really angry. I think he gauged the whole thing, that I wasn't assertive, that I was insecure in the environment I was in, I think he just took advantage of the whole thing.

Presacral neurectomy – the operation is to sever the nerve endings which are positioned in front of the sacrum – the triangular shape at the bottom of the spine. The nerves which are severed are those giving feeling to the pelvic area.

Rosemary's operation took place in 1979 when this operation was relatively rare. It was a fairly common procedure in the 1940s and 1950s and was still being carried out, but less frequently, into the mid-1960s. Cutting the nerve's connection with the spine undoubtedly eases severe dysmenorrhoea (painful periods) and the pain resulting from serious endometriosis in many cases. However, the results are unpredictable, which is why most gynaecologists prefer not to do this operation nowadays.

The operation has recently come back into fashion to some extent, as it is now possible to perform it using a laparoscope. Whilst there are no long-term studies which clearly confirm that pain relief is permanently achieved, a number of women have been helped by this approach.

There has been no evidence to show that presacral neurectomy would adversely affect a woman's fertility one way or the other.

Psychological factors in infertility

Why do so many people tell you that relaxing will make you more likely to conceive?

The myth that relaxing is the solution to fertility problems is so prevalent that it needs to be verified by scientific evidence. The problem with testing these ideas is that they are based on anecdote. One of the common stories about infertility is that a couple's fertility increases after adoption. This is simply not true. Neither is the idea that giving up hope of conception will restore fertility, so there is no point in the infertile tying themselves in knots by pretending to have given up trying.

Infertile women find it deeply upsetting that other people tactlessly write off their pain at childlessness by suggesting they have stressed-out personalities. The urban myths are fed by the fact that much of what happens during conception is still a mystery. The books about infertility are full of stories about people who were thought to have no chance of having a baby, who are suddenly successful. It is very difficult to pinpoint why someone who has suffered infertility for years becomes pregnant. A large amount of infertility remains unexplained and so when a pregnancy happens the doctors are equally at a loss to explain why success came at that moment.

Why would stress be likely to have an effect on fertility?

A woman's menstrual cycle, as well as other aspects of human reproduction, has been shown to be influenced by stress. Many women experience a time in their lives when they miss a period because they are particularly stressed – say because of a bereavement, particularly crucial exams or a new job. Being involuntarily childless is itself a stressful business.

During a period of stress the body's response can interfere with normal hormonal processes. The hypothalamus part of the brain produces a secretion called GnRH (gonadotrophin-releasing hormone) which is essential for the maintenance of a normal menstrual cycle and ovulation. The GnRH causes the release of two other hormones – LH (luteinizing hormone) and FSH (follicle-stimulating hormone) – from the pituitary gland, which in turn stimulate and control the ovaries' ability to produce eggs at the appropriate time.

The normal release of GnRH can be affected by the production of opioid peptides which are also produced by the brain. One sort of opioid peptides are endorphins. Stress is one of the factors that affects the level of opioid peptides. This would be one way in which stress might cause a hormonal imbalance and therefore affect a woman's fertility.

There are several well-known examples which are often quoted of women's reproductive capacity being curtailed during periods of stress. The women who are Kalahari Desert dwellers stop having periods when the food supply is scarce. Whether this is due to stress or malnutrition is not clear. This is not really a very useful comparison to the stress experienced by women in an industrialized society.

A more relevant example, often noticed by infertility specialists, and which may have a psychological explanation is called 'spontaneous healing'. Apparently 30 per cent of all women who go for infertility counselling become pregnant during the talking phase of the therapy, before any medical treatment is given. ('IVF waiting-list pregnancies', Frydman 1987). One of the possible explanations for this may be that stress is decreasing during the counselling sessions – simply the relief of discussing the problem with someone regarded as an expert may have an effect. It should also be remembered that 30 per cent is precisely the percentage of previously 'infertile' women who became pregnant with no treatment or doctor's intervention.

Profession Winston feels that stress is only a minor contributing factor and for most women there are many more important lifestyle factors to be taken into consideration.

What could be other causes of infertility which may be to do with lifestyle?

Can you be too thin to conceive?

It would appear that some women need a certain minimum amount of fat in their body to remain fertile. Women with anorexia nervosa develop amenhorrea (loss of periods) – but even a weight loss of 10 to 15 per cent of a woman's ideal weight can interfere with the menstrual cycle.

The reason for this is a change in hormone secretion patterns. The woman's menstrual cycle is usually restored to normal when her weight increases again.

Can you be too fat?

Obesity can also be a problem: one of the reasons for this is that the fat becomes unable to metabolizse sex hormones. Being overweight can also be a factor in male infertility although many obese men are completely fertile.

Can you be too fit?

Athletes sometimes experience temporary disorders in their menstrual cycles. Running a marathon can potentially interfere with the secretion of GnRH from the hypothalamus and therefore affect the hormones which create the normal ovulation process.

Should you give up alcohol?

Chronic alcohol abuse reduces susceptible men's sperm quality and can also, in exceptional circumstances, reduce a woman's fertility. There does not seem to be any evidence that moderate alcohol consumption has any ill effect.

What about smoking?

Smoking more than 20 cigarettes a day reduces both sperm count and sperm mobility in some but not all men.

Smoking may also put a part in a woman's fertility. One study found that the conception rate in non-smoking women was higher than in smokers. Failure to conceive was three or four times more common in smokers than non-smokers. Another estimation shows that the fertility of smoking women was only about 70 per cent that of non-smokers. The fertility of smokers has also been shown to decrease with an increasing number of cigarettes per day. Other studies have, however, failed to find any adverse effect at all.

Why do some women give up drinking coffee when they are trying to get pregnant?

Caffeine-containing beverages may decrease a woman's ability to conceive. The jury is still out on this question. On the prosecution side the evidence is a study by Wilcox *et al* in 1988 which showed that married women who planned a pregnancy and who drank four or more cups of coffee a day had only an 81 per cent chance of becoming pregnant per cycle compared to women who were not coffee drinkers. This is backed up by another study suggesting that the risk of taking longer than twelve months to conceive was 80 per cent higher for women who drank a lot of coffee than for those who didn't.

However, in defence if coffee, a study carried out around the same time of 2817 women showed no difference in the time taken to conceive at all, nor any association with caffeine intake by women in 1818 infertile patients.

Does environmental pollution affect fertility?

There have been one or two studies that have shown a link between infertility in men and women and exposure to toxic substances. There is no doubt at all that some chemicals – such as insecticides – and some drugs, such as cancer drugs or cannabis, have an adverse effect on both male and female fertility.

Will taking the pill affect fertility later?

Many women express the worry that a long period on the pill or using other methods of contraception will affect their ability to conceive. The pill's long-term effect on the body's own hormone production would seem to be the cause of most women's anxieties.

The medical trials which have been carried out all agree that there is very little risk to a woman's future fertility from use of the pill. Doctors worry about other aspects of long-term use, but not fertility. Most women return to having regular periods six months after stopping taking the pill. Less than one in a hundred women find they have no periods for longer than six months after finishing taking the pill. Neither is there a connection between the particular type of pill which women take and the loss of periods (amenhorrea). 'Fertility after contraception or abortion' (Review) *Fertility and Sterility*, Oct 1990 – Huggins GR and Cullins VE.

Contraceptives are indirectly linked with infertility because they allow women to delay the time when they have children. We know that a woman's fertility decreases with age. By the time she is in her thirties and trying for a first pregnancy her fertility has reduced simply because of her age. Also, if she has been taking the pill since her teens she may not know that her cycle was not normal because the problem would have been disguised by the effects of the contraception. So even though the symptoms might have been there much earlier, for her the knowledge of any abnormality is always associated with the time when she gave up the pill.

Does diet have any effect?

Being generally healthy means you are more likely to conceive but beyond that it would be difficult to associate particular foods with fertility. The research in this area never seems to be particularly convincing one way or the other. Flimsy evidence in research findings then get turned into snippets of information for newspapers or magazines and becomes misinformation – not exactly wrong but not the full picture either.

Here is an example: An article in *Science News*, 12 March 1994 suggests that women who would like to get pregnant but have failed to conceive may like to review how big a role dairy products play in their diet. A team of researchers in the States and Finland have shown that where per capita milk consumption is highest, women tend to experience the sharpest age-related fall-off in fertility. In countries like Thailand, where people hardly eat dairy products at all, fertility in women aged 35 to 39 is only 26 per cent lower than peak rates (at age 25 to 29). By contrast, in Australia and the UK, where dairy products are a large part of most people's diet, average fertility by age 35 to 39 is fully 82 per cent below peak rates.

This sounds very interesting until you realize how little it says. There are hundreds of other factors such as marriage customs, divorce rates and contraceptive use which could be affecting these results. In the meantime lots of desperate women will be 'reviewing the role dairy products play in their diet' – some of them will become pregnant and thus a new food fad for the infertile will be in full swing.

CHAPTER 3

TESTS

For each of the women the next stage was to find out what could be done. Tests are carried out for two reasons: firstly to find out the cause of the infertility and secondly to help the doctors decide on the most appropriate form of treatment.

Both physically and emotionally this can be a stressful time: some couples find the medical procedures are very invasive and the sheer strain of constantly being under pressure about sex and fertility becomes a problem in itself.

At the end of this chapter some of the more recent developments in tests and diagnostic techniques are described.

Miranda was referred for treatment to the Hammersmith Hospital in London. At that time Clive was a hospital manager there and knew the clinic had a good reputation. Miranda continued to hope that the medical assistance would prove to be unnecessary and she would fall pregnant naturally. She and Clive still did not have a complete explanation of why conception was not happening.

I had to prepare myself for the intrusion that is involved in the tests. It is a bit of an ordeal because you're in and out of the hospital, it seems like every five minutes, with continual probes and scans. I had to go through a process of consciously accepting that I was going to do all this. No woman would willingly have probes stuck up her vagina twenty times. I had to remind myself by going through that mental process whereby I chose to do it again.

First of all the GP did basic tests on both of us: blood tests for me to check my hormone levels and Clive had to ejaculate into a bottle and it was rushed off to the hospital for analysis. They also looked into my thyroid function. Later, at the hospital, they monitored my menstrual cycle in even more detail. I had regular blood tests over two cycles.

The consultant has always been extremely kind and has always explained things carefully to Clive and me. He showed us the x-ray and it was all really clear. One good and interesting thing about infertility treatment is that you are able to see a lot of things yourself. When you have the ultrasound scans and the x-rays and then actual embryos, you don't have to be trained to see it, you can clearly see everything: the cavity, the lining, tubes, embryos and the sperm on the cervical mucus test. It's also very easy to understand and to be involved in it if you want to be.

When you are having a monitored cycle, ultrasound scans are a part of the process; they are vaginal scans for which you don't have to have a full bladder. A probe goes into the vagina and then you can watch the ultrasound screen. They can image the uterus, the lining and the ovaries.

The hysteroscopy and laparoscopy were done together and I had to have a general anaesthetic. With a hysteroscopy they look inside the uterus to see if there are any polyps and to check the healthiness of the lining. They use a fibre-optic tube. With the laparoscopy they can check the healthiness of the organs and tubes, so they can see adhesions or scarring and detect endometriosis.

When I had my laparoscopy they said my ovaries were polycystic. They looked kind of smooth and as if they had a pearly white coating. They also said I had one or two little patches of endometriosis, which I understand is common in women of my age who haven't had children – nothing to worry about necessarily.

For the laparoscopy you are generally invited to stay in hospital for a couple of nights. I opted to go in as a day case because I thought the less time I spent in hospital the happier I'd be. They agreed to that. It didn't hurt very much and I recovered very quickly. One thing they didn't tell me was that I was going to have a hysteroscopy – where they look in the womb as well – at the same time, which is a sensible addition. So that was a surprise when I woke up; I was bleeding because the operation disturbs the lining of the womb. It wasn't a problem and it's good that they look at all these things.

During the laparoscopy gas is inserted into the abdominal cavity through a needle placed in the navel. Once the gas has created a space, a telescope can be inserted to allow the surgeon a good view. Photographs can be taken via the telescope. During the twenty to forty minutes the operation takes, the surgeon will look at the uterus for scarring and adhesions, test the fallopian tubes to see if they are open and look at the ovaries.

A laparoscopy may be carried out in the second half of the cycle; if it is, the ovaries can be examined to see if ovulation has taken place. Afterwards the woman will be left with two small dressings on the abdomen. One covers the single stitch in the navel and the other a tiny hole near the pubic-hair line. The second hole is used to place other tiny probes into the abdominal cavity which may be required to get a better view.

Hysteroscopy is a rather different procedure. Here, a fibre optic telescope is used to look inside the uterus.

I had to have an x-ray, a hysterosalpingogram, which was very unpleasant and painful. That was tricky because you have to have it at the right time in your cycle, and they don't do them every day. So it took me some months to be able to do it on the right day. Also, quite rightly, they won't do it if there is the slightest possibility that you're pregnant. I got turned away one time because I had not used contraception in the early part of my cycle. They were right of course, but it was very frustrating. When I eventually got round to having it, it was about three months later. They put dye up into your tubes under some pressure and x-ray, so they can see the cavity of the uterus and the tubes and see if they're blocked. I found it painful, which surprised me because they had said it would just be a bit uncomfortable.

They put a little tube through the cervix and that passes the fluid through the tubes. Most women, I think, find it slightly uncomfortable but I found it very unpleasant. But that wasn't the doctors' fault, they were very gentle. You can't feel the x-ray itself, but I felt the fluid passing through which made my uterus and tubes spasm and that was what hurt me. I seemed to have terrible cramping.

The fluid is blue dye which shows up on the x-ray. If your tubes are clear some of the dye shoots out of the ends into the cavity – and if no dye comes through then you know you've got tubal problems. (*Doctors refer to the tubes as being 'patent', meaning 'open'.*) Afterwards it was mildly uncomfortable for a few hours, nothing serious. You discharge some of the rest of it – I had a bit of an odd discharge for a day or two and then when my next period came it looked a bit odd. So you're aware of it for a while and then it's nothing.

I found the hysterosalpingogram a particularly emotionally distressing test. I think it's hard to separate the physical from the emotional. I don't know why. It just hurt.

The hysterosalpingogram is an x-ray of the uterus and fallopian tubes. During the x-ray a little dye is placed into the uterus and x-rays are taken. In the majority of cases it causes little or no pain. The fallopian tubes can be tested to see if they are open. If there is a blockage, this shows up on the x-ray. The outline of the dye also appears on the x-ray as the shadow of the inside of the uterus.

*You do not have to have an anaesthetic and you do not have to
stay in hospital over night.*

I felt I was well prepared for the treatment. I always found at the
Hammersmith that they are very careful about giving good
explanations about what is going to happen. I've heard lots of stories
about women who have been at hospitals which haven't done the
simple and basic tests and just missed obvious things like polyps in the
uterus or whatever. That's one of the things that makes the
Hammersmith so good – they don't cut any corners. Just because
they've found one problem, they don't stop there, they check
everything.

I also had a cervical mucus test. You have to go to the hospital a few
hours after having made love. They will collect some mucus from your
cervix, and look at it. They should be able to see sperm moving
actively. It's a double test to see if your mucus is suitable, whether the
sperm survive and can swim vigorously, and whether the two things fit
together. You can tell a lot from that test. I had that repeated just to be
on the safe side.

*The post-coital test is usually carried out, as the name suggests, the
morning after the couple have made love. A sample of fluid is
taken from the woman's cervix during a normal internal
examination (the kind you have for a smear). The fluid is then
checked under a microscope to see how the sperm are reacting to
the cervical mucus. The test is usually carried out shortly before
ovulation should take place.*

*Some people have a compatibility problem. Couples shouldn't be
unduly worried if this test has poor results. There are many reasons
why the test might show a poor result which are not due to
incompatibility. Good practice guidelines suggest the test may
occasionally need to be repeated several times.*

The whole period of tests took a few months. I don't remember
becoming despondent. Funnily enough, it was at the very first scan at
the hospital that the doctor told me I had polycystic ovaries. So I had a
diagnosis right away. Because I knew from the beginning I could start
to think for myself what that might mean. I don't remember my
emotions in detail, but I think that at that time I was still hoping that I
would get pregnant myself, and that I wouldn't end up having to have
treatment. I was also always hoping that my next homeopathic remedy
would work.

I think the homeopathy helped me in that I was healthier and happier, and was able to cope quite well. It was tough because the homeopathy never made me fertile, but I am convinced that it helped in that it strengthened me so that I would be in really good shape if I did other treatment. Who knows what would have happened at a future stage. It certainly alleviated some of the effects of the treatment. For instance, after the laparoscopy, I took remedies to help myself recover because I had some bruising. I didn't take painkillers, I just took homeopathic remedies. I also had a sore throat where the tube had been stuck down for the anaesthetic, and I took a remedy which cleared it up immediately.

I seemed to recover after the anaesthetics fairly quickly as well. I got used to the idea of them – I knew if I was going to pursue this I needed to. By this time I was prepared to go through with IVF if I had to. I had gradually acquired books about it and shopped around for information. I had also joined ISSUE. (*See the list of organizations at the back of the book*.)

After several appointments with her GP, referrals to Charing Cross Hospital and one consultation through BUPA with an infertility specialist, Liz eventually decided to try to have her infertility investigated thoroughly. She was referred to the Reproductive Medicine Unit at Queen Charlotte's Hospital. By this time Liz was in her mid-thirties and although she and Andy had been trying for a few years they had not achieved a pregnancy.

The first time I went to Queen Charlotte's I went in the wrong entrance. I found myself in the maternity unit. There is such a difference between that entrance and the Reproductive Medicine Unit. Suddenly I was bombarded with dinky little clothes for babies, balloons with welcoming messages to the newly born written on them and endless booties and romper suits. So I thought, 'Well perhaps I'm going to be successful.' I told the receptionist that I was looking for Reproductive Medicine and she said, 'You're in the wrong building; it's over there.'

I was in such a tizzy I went and had a cup of coffee. I suppose I felt at that time that I was coming to be investigated and I might have a baby, in fact, I probably would have one. The tizzy was about having to have internal examinations, and blood tests and hormones taken and probably an x-ray of my pituitary gland. It's just that everything that I had was going to be looked at under a microscope. People who get pregnant naturally don't have any of this. It seems so unfair. It had happened to me several times by this stage. I'd been through it at Charing Cross and privately and now here I was again.

The Reproductive Medicine part of the hospital is much less welcoming than the maternity unit, nothing cheerful about the entrance. However, when you get up to the clinic you are bombarded with pictures of IVF babies, the success stories. It made me feel that I wanted one of those too.

I went two or three times for consultations about what the problems were and what tests were available. Sometimes I would have to bring a sample of Andy's sperm, nestled under my coat to keep it warm, and deliver it to the laboratory technician who took it away to do the necessaries.

The last consultation I remember sitting with Andy in the seats in the corridor. I think we were holding hands while we waited. I said that I didn't know how long it would take. Andy was so uncomfortable he couldn't sit still and he kept saying, 'I've got to get to the office. I must get back.' He was so tense. I said, 'Oh, all right then. You go. I'll wait for the result.' But he said, 'No, no, I'll stay.' He is so healthy, and he just hates hospitals. He just can't bear to be in one.

About ten minutes later a consultant walked down and called us in. He then talked to us about Andy's sperm. He said it was healthy in terms of there being plenty of little wiggly bits. But they actually didn't wiggle very much. And that is when one of the consultants said, 'We'd like you to go home, Mr Morris, and produce some sperm samples. If you could masturbate or make love to your wife twenty times this weekend.'

He was deadly serious. I didn't say a thing at the time because I couldn't believe what I was hearing. We're both over thirty and we are not in our first flight of passion.

So we left. We went to collect the car and I drove Andy to the station to get a train to work. I don't think we said a word to each other all the way. That was the last doctor I ever went to see about it. I didn't know what else to do about it. I knew it was hopeless after that. I knew Andy couldn't do what they asked and I knew that I couldn't help him to do that that often. The consultant wanted us to try to produce an awful lot of sperm and see if it would swim any faster.

Afterwards I started to wonder if I had heard it right. Half the trouble with being infertile is that you wonder if you are doing the right thing. Several times I have come away from doctors thinking, 'Well is that the right thing, did they really say that?' I also felt pessimistic. I couldn't see how on earth we were going to accomplish this. It's not how we spend our weekends, it's not how we make love. It just felt completely unnatural.

I suppose there was some consolation in the fact that I now knew it was not just my problem. It meant we shared the responsibility and there was no blame. We left feeling so inadequate. I can't see how, unless you're a rampant seventeen-year-old man, you're going to be able to produce sperm at that rate. The feeling of inadequacy for Andy came not from the physical problem with the sperm. It was the implicit criticism of his virility. We also felt failures because we couldn't be a family.

So at this point we thought, 'This is going to be too much of a strain on us and our relationship.' We had only got to the stage of producing sperm samples; it wasn't even close to having a baby. We knew other couples were willing to go through much more. But for Andy and me, we just didn't want to go through all that shit.

When semen analysis is carried out the sperm is examined to see if it is adequate to achieve pregnancy. Firstly the volume of semen is measured. A normal amount is about a teaspoonful. If the volume is low, the man may be producing too few secretions, but sometimes this just indicates that part of the sample has not been collected at ejaculation. A large amount of semen is not always a good indication because it sometimes means that the sperm is too dilute.

The laboratory will also check for the number of sperm. There should be more than forty million in each millilitre. Some men have significantly lower counts and still remain fully fertile.

The sperm motility (which is what Liz discussed with her consultant) should show that at least 40 per cent of the sperm are moving about.

At least 65 per cent of the sperm should look normal under the microscope. The laboratory will also sometimes test whether the sperm get stuck together and for any indications of infection, such as too many white blood cells or bacteria. Other problems may be detected by testing for chemicals such as fructose and for antibodies which can act by attacking the sperm. It is very important that several semen samples are taken into account over a reasonable period of time because men's sperm count can vary from test to test. This is sometimes due to stress and other factors. It would be extremely unusual for a consultant to suggest a man should produce 20 samples over a weekend.

After her first laparoscopy Sheila was diagnosed as having endometriosis. She began taking a drug treatment called Danazol. Here she describes what it felt like to go through the process of treatment for the endometriosis and on to the further tests to try and solve her and her partner's fertility problems.

I had no idea of the traumatic journey I was beginning and the events which followed still leave me with a sense of total disbelief even after all this time. I don't think I understood it at the time, but I felt I was just being dragged along by events. It worked just like a treadmill. You go along a certain path, and there is an inevitability which it is almost impossible to divert from. When and how do you make a decision to stop? That was the really, really difficult thing, to make that decision.

It took over my life, but I feel it was inevitable. People ask now why I let it, but I had no choice in a way, because it seemed to be set that it would. I was trying to find out when I ovulated by taking my temperature every morning before I even got up. So it was unavoidable that I should be thinking about getting pregnant every moment.

I also had these ideas in my head that if we didn't make love for a week before I ovulated then there would be more sperm available. When I look back on it, it was horrible. I don't know if I was put in the same situation now, knowing what I know, that I'd react in the same way. I almost think the obsessiveness is inevitable from what I've read about other women's experiences.

Altogether I had four laparoscopies and also a hysterosalpingogram. It didn't seem to take ages to be referred for the various tests and treatments, though I know for some women the waiting seems endless. It was months rather than years.

I was quite anxious the first time I went for a laparoscopy. I worried that it would be painful, which it was, although people say it's not. It was extremely painful. But I also felt quite relieved that something was happening and hopeful that I might find the answer to the problem.

Since I had that laparoscopy the procedure has changed – the last one I had was about a year ago and I was in and out in about a day. The first time I had it done, about five years ago, it was much more complicated. I had to stay in overnight and I remember feeling a bit frightened because I had never had a general anaesthetic before. I couldn't eat for twelve hours beforehand, as with any general anaesthetic, and I was given a pre-med. It's only about a fifteen-minute operation I think, but when I came out my tummy was very sore. I felt quite sick and sore for about three to four days afterwards.

The pain afterwards was a reaction to my abdomen being expanded with gas. It feels like really severe indigestion. My throat was usually quite sore as well, but that was due to the tube they put down your windpipe for the anaesthetic. I don't think I ever really reacted badly to the general anaesthetic, I just remember feeling very sleepy. The first time was worse than with subsequent laparoscopies. I don't know quite why that was, or whether they have improved the type of anaesthetic they use.

As I went on with the tests and treatments my relationship with my husband started to deteriorate. In 1984, when I got married, I really thought it was the best thing that had ever happened to me. I remember feeling really hopeful; I was with someone with whom I got on really well. There were about two years of this feeling of great hopefulness before the terrible loneliness of the infertility treatments. This loneliness was partly to do with the emotional side-effects of hormonal drugs, partly to do with my relationship with my husband and partly to do with my own feelings of failure and inadequacy at the time.

When I found out about the endometriosis I was prescribed Danazol. The tablets made me feel physically very bad, and I also put on a lot of weight so I felt very unattractive, and quite ill. My feelings about myself and my sexuality got worse the further I went with the infertility treatment. I took the Danazol for about nine months, went back for another laparoscopy and was told that the endometriosis had reduced and that we could start trying again to conceive. (*One of the effects of Danazol is to suppress the menstrual cycle so it means there is no chance of conceiving while taking it.*) If nothing happened I was to return in six months. Nothing did. There did not seem to be any permanent damage done to my fallopian tubes from the endometriosis. I was also trying at this point to change my lifestyle and to improve my health generally by diet and exercise to see if that would improve my fertility – I don't know if that also had a positive effect.

They then put me on another type of medication, Clomid, to encourage ovulation. I just remember the treatments were a very lonely experience because my husband wasn't able to support me. I don't remember having any physical side-effects from the Clomid, but it was about this time I started to take my temperature every day, the moment I woke up, to check for ovulation. Then I would carefully record it all. This was the only time I had ever really been in touch with my body's cycle and the side-effect of that was that sex became fairly mechanical. Certainly from my point of view I became very obsessive about it. It was quite hard for my husband to understand that. Altogether the treatments started to have a disastrous effect on our marriage. It was two years into the treatment that my husband's sperm count was investigated and found to be low.

He went into a process of denial, he just wanted to assume that I would be able to have our child. He seemed to get annoyed with me for being obsessive. But for me this was a real cause for irritation towards him because he kept saying he wanted a child but he wasn't doing anything about it. I was the one going through all these processes. He was supposed to do the cold water treatment but I had to take responsibility for that as well. I think he thought that I was being a bit extreme when I started taking care of my diet, and not wanting to drink, or have tea or coffee. He had no faith in any of that. I think he got rather annoyed by the mechanics of it; sex could never just be spontaneous and without doubt that put a tremendous strain on us.

The principle behind temperature charts is that a woman's temperature rises slightly after ovulation. Each morning the woman is required to take her temperature before she gets out of bed. She then records what the thermometer says after one minute under her tongue on a chart which shows the month.

Professor Winston recognizes the pitfalls for many couples like Sheila and her husband of using this method: it can be unreliable and many women who have perfectly normal ovulation cycles show no difference in temperature at all. He also disapproves of it because some women are led to believe that their temperature chart will tell them when they are at their most fertile and use it to time intercourse. In fact the best time to conceive is twelve to forty-eight hours before ovulation – so this is before the temperature starts to rise.

The advantages of temperature charting are that it is cheap, for some women it is a fairly convenient way of checking ovulation, and there is some benefit in feeling that there is something over which you can take control.

The alternative is to examine the cervical mucus at different times during the menstrual cycle. At the time of ovulation the mucus production reaches a peak and the mucus looks and feels rather like the uncooked white of an egg. Immediately after ovulation, when a woman is no longer fertile, the mucus thickens and then dries up almost completely.

Examining mucus is very unreliable as a sign of ovulation – for example, vaginal infections or sexual secretions can cause confusion by masking the changes in the mucus. It also varies from woman to woman, with some very fertile women producing no mucus at all.

Vivienne and Chester were still living in Germany where they worked in the Armed Forces. Vivienne had been on antibiotics for six months, to try to combat the inflammation caused by pelvic inflammatory disease, and had then had a second laparoscopy. The dye which was inserted during the operation never travelled through the fallopian tube, and they realized that they were going to have difficulty conceiving. The pelvic inflammatory disease was continuing to cause swelling and discomfort and Vivienne was taking strong painkillers permanently.

During the laparoscopy they put gas into my abdomen so they could see what the extent of the damage from inflammation was. I think they put a catheter in and they feed dye into the fallopian tubes. You can actually have it under x-ray facilities, but they decided to take me into theatre. They wanted to have a look round to see whether the infection and everything had started to clear up. Basically the dye went in and went through the tubes, but it didn't come out of the other end. That was obviously quite distressing, because before there was always a bit of hope that the antibiotics would have worked. But I was ovulating normally so the doctor suggested we go away and practise.

That brought its own complications. We hadn't really decided to start a family immediately. We would ideally have liked to wait two or three years because we were living abroad and I was still only twenty-seven. We were quite happy to build up a little bit of a nest egg. But because of the urgency felt by the doctors we then felt we were under quite a lot of pressure to try and conceive. But it wasn't really what we wanted at that particular time.

We felt we had to take the advice of the specialist. He just said, 'Look, no more contraception, no more waiting around. It's a case of trying now. Go away and practise and let nature take its course.' Once we got used to the idea, we were OK about it. Again it was back to not really making that decision for ourselves. Infertility always seems to be about having choice taken away from you. I felt under quite a bit of pressure.

Then the consultant said that although the dye used during the laparoscopy didn't reach the end of the fallopian tubes, it does sometimes have the effect of clearing them a bit and forcing things along. So he was hoping that having had that treatment, my tubes would open up. Although it didn't look terribly promising on the results of the test, I didn't feel he shut off every avenue of possibility. I still had a lot of discomfort from the infection, that hadn't reduced at all.

Then the specialist asked me if I'd thought about tubal surgery. My husband didn't want me to go through with anything else because of all the discomfort. But I thought if the gynaecologist was prepared to give me a go at surgery, then we should have one go, so at least I could say I had a try. If I hadn't gone through that, I think my feelings of failure would really have been even worse. I think it made me feel a lot better that I could have a go at this surgery.

This was about 1981. During that year I had a positive pregnancy result. I went to the doctor who said, 'Yes, you're pregnant.' I don't know why he actually examined me but I remember him saying to me that there should be no reason why this shouldn't be a straightforward, normal pregnancy. I was prepared to give up work; prepared to do anything . . . and then two or three days later that was the end of that. It's still very painful to think about it. It's one of those things where you want to turn the clock back but you can't. I think, 'Well why did the gynaecologist examine me?' but that's perfectly normal and wouldn't bring on a miscarriage. It was just very, very sad.

My husband told a few people about the pregnancy and we still meet people now who say, 'I hear you've got a little girl.' I just say, 'No, we haven't actually.' I did tell him not to tell anybody in case anything happened, but he was so pleased and so excited, that you couldn't take that away from him. So that was all a bit traumatic yet again. I thought, 'If I got pregnant once there is no reason why I can't get pregnant again.' I look back on it all now and think, 'Did I make all that up?' But I didn't, for a few brief moments I was actually pregnant.

We then said we'd have a go at this tubal surgery. For this last lot of surgery, I'd obviously got quite worked-up, so they had me in for ten days beforehand. The consultant actually had me in for bed-rest and TLC really, because mentally I had got quite twitchy and things. I thought the surgery would be wonderful, because he was going to cut out the bad bits of the fallopian tubes and try to repair the damage. This was quite pioneering surgery in 1982.

Unfortunately it all came to nothing. I felt complete and utter devastation. When I came back from theatre I thought I was fine, I was all ready for the fresh hope the tubal surgery would bring. But the consultant had told my husband that he had taken a look at my uterus and tubes and that things were still in such a bad state that he just opened me up and closed me again. He said there were adhesions and all sorts of things and he didn't really feel that it was safe to intervene and do any sort of surgery.

I can honestly say that I think the consultant we were dealing with was as upset as I was because he had got to know us over a long period of time. My husband was really, really good but he felt we'd done everything that was surgically possible. For some reason, and I can't really say why – IVF was very new – I said, 'That's it, if we can't have a baby naturally, and we obviously can't have a baby with help, then that's it.' We felt we had to close the door on it because it was beginning to take over.

I think Chester was even more aware that it was taking over our lives than me. I was beginning to realize that if we didn't take things carefully this need for our own baby was potentially damaging. You have to look at what you do have. I did not have a malignant tumour. Also, we have a really good marriage, and I thought if we're not careful, this is going to wreck what we've already built.

The doctors were quite keen for us to think seriously about adoption. Chester said fairly early on, 'If we can't have a baby of our own we don't want anyone else's, do we?' He doesn't remember saying that to me because I suppose it was said off the cuff. So I felt then that not only did I have to come to terms with not having a baby of our own, but not ever having a baby. Chester and I did discuss adoption, but I felt after he said that to me that it had to be a joint decision and very much a 100 per cent thing. I think half of me was a little bit worried about rocking the boat. I didn't really feel that adoption was what I wanted. Since I'd worked in maternity and had been a nanny I felt I might be a little clinical towards the child, and we'll never know because we made that decision. We didn't make it overnight, we sat and discussed it.

By then we knew we were going to Hong Kong. That was something really very exciting to look forward to – a fresh start.

Laura was becoming very impatient with her doctors. They did not seem to share her sense of urgency about becoming pregnant. She had waited months to have all of the coil finally removed from her uterus by D and C and then she had been put on Danazol. The drug suppresses ovulation and so pregnancy can only happen after the treatment is over. During this time her husband Robert had not been given a sperm test.

When I went back they said they should do two things: one was a sperm test on my husband, Robert; and the other one was a post-coital test to make sure that my mucus was a friendly environment for Robert's sperm. By this time sex was quite ghastly. It was all rather mechanical – we were always thinking, 'Are we going to have a baby this month or not?' It had become so regimented that we wouldn't do anything until the middle of the month, and then we had to make sure we did, then we'd get pissed off on day twenty-eight when another period came around.

For the post-coital test it was even worse. We had to make love at eight in the morning and then I had to get myself ready for a smear test at ten, after the sperm had been inside for exactly two hours. At this stage you do begin to feel a bit like a laboratory animal, with all the potential charm of intercourse completely annihilated.

It was very difficult to talk about it. I think we both resigned ourselves to the fact that this was what we had to do. I think once you've had fertility problems, it's ridiculous to even begin to think that you can look at sex normally. Because what you want is a baby, and the way to get a baby is through sex. So you don't even come near to having normal, natural, loving sex. It's all about timing.

Then I was given the charts to take my temperature, to know exactly when I was ovulating. If my temperature shot up I'd be asked if we made love two days before. The whole thing is really technical and intrusive.

I started the temperature charts for one month but I just gave up. I found the mucus test much more efficient. That at least showed you when you were ovulating rather than telling you two days later that you had ovulated. After that when I went back and said I didn't want to be on Danazol and that I was sick of taking my temperature, the doctor told me there was good news: 'Your husband's sperm count was not at all good.' In fact, having looked at my husband's sperm, the doctor said that the major cause of the infertility was the low sperm count.

I was so bloody irritated by this because for two years it had been seen entirely as my responsibility. It wasn't that I wanted to share any blame, but I wanted to share responsibility. I also felt that the IUD, extra D and C, the Danazol and hormonal testing were all a waste of time, and if they had pinpointed that earlier, we could have found a more constructive route to go down.

I felt very protective towards Robert but very irritated that the count had not been tested before. I think that every couple going in should be treated equally as though they are both potentially the cause of the problem. Whatever happens, I think it's really much better if you go in together and they tell you that there are a number of factors which cause infertility and there are some we don't even know about. Of one in eight couples who are infertile, they will not know why. It always seems as if the medical profession just swings the spotlight of responsibility on to the woman. If that doesn't work then they start to look at the man. I think that for any couple going through it, a more practical and kind approach is necessary. Then you would be finding out the problems together. You would also be treated as equals. With the broken-up IUD, the evidence of endometriosis, and one blocked tube, I had felt that all these things were conspiring against my fertility. All of these palled in comparison to a very low sperm count.

The presacral neurectomy performed by a Harley Street surgeon during the late 1970s had stopped Rosemary's period pains. But it may also have severely affected her ability to have a baby. The consultant at King's College Hospital had told her quite categorically that in his opinion she would not be able to have children.

Because he'd been so positive that there wasn't any chance I almost accepted it. I thought, 'Well, it's so final there's nothing I can do about it.' I was in absolute despair but I did accept it.

Both David and I had to go back to see the doctor as outpatients to the infertility clinic. I think it was at that point he said to me that there was the possibility that I could have microsurgery on the tube. He hadn't been able to find one of my fallopian tubes. But the other one, although it was in a bad state, was possibly reparable by microsurgery. He said if I could come up with the name of a surgeon he would start the procedure to make it happen. We left it that he would write to an eminent surgeon to fix up an appointment about microsurgery.

The last thing I had done at this time was a hysterosalpingogram, where they put dye into the fallopian tube. They were surprised that although the damage seemed extensive the dye passed through the tube fairly easily. I was still in a frame of mind where I felt pretty hopeless about conceiving because the other doctor had been so adamant.

A few weeks went by and I went to see my GP because I couldn't hear very well. One of my ears was blocked with wax and needed syringing. I had it done and I just got up out of the chair to go and I said, 'Oh, by the way, perhaps I'd better mention I haven't been feeling very well.' He said, 'In what way?' and I said, 'I can't really put my finger on it, I'm tired and I just don't feel well. I've missed a period by a week or so but I know that I'm not pregnant because I've had investigations done.' He replied, 'Well fine, but we'll do a pregnancy test first because then we can eliminate that and go on to other things'.

I phoned a few days later and asked the receptionist and she said, 'Yes Mrs Thornton, your test is positive.' I didn't take that on board at all and I said, 'Oh fine, but that obviously isn't me because I've been told I can't become pregnant. It's the wrong name or the wrong address'. She checked again, then she said, 'No, it's definite, that's right'.

Anyway, I think I phoned them back and I was shaking like a leaf by this time. I phoned about three or four times and I said, 'There's definitely some mistake, perhaps they'd got muddled at the hospital,' and she said it was very unlikely; she was rather kind really. I think she was quite amused.

I decided to walk to the doctor's and I asked the receptionist if it would be possible to have a word with the doctor because I was sure there was some mistake, and she said, 'Well, we'll see what we can do.' So I think I went that same day and saw the GP and he said, 'No, there isn't any mistake, it's definitely you,' and he said that sometimes these things happen, especially in the field of fertility; we haven't got the last word and sometimes we can say there's no hope and this is how it turns out. I just couldn't believe it and I really did think it was a miracle, because it was. There's a school close to where we lived, and I can remember stopping on my way home from the doctor's and standing, watching the children in the playground and thinking it would all be all right after all.

I waited until David came home because I didn't want to tell him over the phone. When I told him he had the same reaction as me – he just couldn't believe it and like me he thought it was a miracle and we were absolutely over the moon really. I think most people are delighted when they're told that the test is positive, but if you've been told there's absolutely no chance that you will ever have a child and then it's positive, it's just incredible. I don't think any of us could believe it really.

We bought books for children's names and we chose Emily for a girl and Thomas for a boy. We saw life in front of us with, if not children, at least this one child and I think I was at my happiest. I felt that it was all coming together and that the identity I'd looked for was at last really close. I felt part of it was being with David, I felt that's where I belonged, that he was definitely the right person. I absolutely loved Richmond, where we lived, so it was the right place. And now I was going to have a baby so I just felt that everything was coming together and it was a really, really happy time. I was absolutely content and I remember thinking that I might not ever feel like that again because I might never be pregnant again.

Other tests

Not all clinics use the same methods of testing. Some have a definite policy of keeping tests to a minimum so that the small budget they have can be spent on treatment.

What is an endometrial biopsy?

This is a test which would be performed during the second half of the menstrual cycle. A tiny piece of endometrial tissue is examined under a microscope to reveal whether the lining of the uterus is responding to progesterone. Progesterone production is triggered by ovulation and it plays an important role in sustaining a pregnancy in the early stages. An endometrial biopsy is sometimes carried out at the same time as a laparoscopy.

What does ovarian ultrasound do?

Ultrasound works by sending ultrasonic sound waves through the body. The echoes can be turned into an image on a television screen. Ultrasound has made an enormous difference to the doctor's ability to monitor pregnancies. Originally women had to arrive for the ultrasound appointment with a full bladder because the sound waves produced a clearer image through water. The machines have continued to improve over the years and now it is not usually necessary to have a full bladder while the ultrasound is being carried out. Many clinics now use vaginal ultrasound – the ultrasound probe is inserted into the vagina instead of placing it on the abdomen. It is a very useful and accurate way to monitor the process of ovulation – detecting the follicular growth and the rupture of the eggs, it will also reveal polycystic ovaries and early pregnancy.

What hormones are looked for in blood tests?

Depending on her symptoms a woman may have her levels of hormones measured, in blood or urine tests, usually two or three times during a cycle. The standard tests are for progesterone, LH (luteinizing hormone) and FSH (follicle stimulating hormone). The results of the tests are then compared with those for a group of women who are known to be ovulating normally. Sometimes doctors will suggest hormone profiles for oestrogen, testosterone, prolactin and thyroid dysfunction. These may be abnormal in particular conditions causing ovulatory failure and are done if these conditions are suspected.

Developments in laparoscopic techniques

Laparoscopy is the surgical technique which allows the gynaecologist to insert a small telescope into the abdominal cavity. Professor Winston says in *Getting Pregnant* – 'It is true to say that laparoscopy – far more than test-tube baby treatment or any other development – has been the most revolutionary advance in infertility diagnosis and treatment.'

In recent years the technology has been refined, with ever smaller telescopes and more innovative ways of inserting them. These are some of the variations which may become more commonly used:

Hysteroscopy – This may be carried out after a hysterosalpingogram (x-ray with dye) if an abnormality is suspected. The hysteroscopy is a telescope which goes inside the uterus and can show the inside wall of the uterus, including the part where the fallopian tube begins (tubal ostium). It would be used to look for adhesions, stenosis (narrowing of the tubes), polyps (fleshy growths in the uterus) or myomas (fibroids). All of these can cause problems and prevent a successful pregnancy.

Tuboscopy – This is a way of examining the inside of the fallopian tube using a very fine telescope – it is usually done by insertion through the abdominal wall while the patient is under anaesthetic. The telescope is only 3mm in diameter and would be used to look at the ovarian end of the fallopian tube to diagnose areas of scarring or damage to the tube.

Falloposcopy – This is a similar technique but the telescopic tube is inserted through the vagina into the uterus. It is an even smaller telescope (0.5mm) which gives it the disadvantage of not providing such a clear picture. However, it has the great advantage of not requiring an incision into the abdomen and therefore the test could be performed as an outpatient procedure. A study which was carried out at the University of Palermo, Italy, claims that the falloposcopy has the advantage of visualizing the entire tube whilst also protecting the tube and the equipment from damage. Conventional methods have been unable to provide a way of examining the inside wall of the fallopian tube (tubal lumen) and the junction where it becomes the uterus (endo salpinx at the utero-tubal ostium). Around the endoscope (camera eye) a tubular-shaped membrane is laid all along the wall of the tube.

This equipment allows the specialists to diagnose more precisely what the blockages might be. Before they would be relying on the shadow outline of the uterus and tubes, which could be shown on the X-ray screen by inserting dye into the cavity.

If sperm is foreign to a woman's body why does her immune system not attack it?

This is one of the most fascinating mysteries of the miracle of conception and pregnancy. Some women's body's are not sperm-friendly environments and this makes them infertile.

Quite a lot of research has been carried out recently into the role of antibodies and the acceptance of sperm as a foreign substance to the body. ('Antiidiotypic Antibodies to Sperm in Fertile Women', *Journal of Clinical Investigation*, November 1993, Albert Einstein College of Medicine, The Bronx NY)

The body's response to foreign substances is to produce antibodies which attack viruses, bacteria etc. It is quite normal for this to happen in a woman's body as a response to a man's sexual secretions. But the immune system is extremely sophisticated and in blood tests carried out on fertile women it was also found that they had anti-antibodies – these attack the plain antibodies and therefore neutralize their effect. This could give many clues to as yet unexplained infertility. It may be that women who suffer from infertility don't develop the anti-antibodies and therefore the sperm has no protection against the anti-sperm antibodies which attack them. Men can also form anti-sperm antibodies and it is thought that perhaps as much as 30 per cent of unexplained infertility could be due to this defect.

The researchers are experimenting with injections of gamma globulins from fertile women which may result in a treatment. Gamma globulins are injections of groups of antibodies – sometimes you have them before visiting particular foreign countries to protect you from viruses and bacteria you would not have been exposed to before. However, this work is still at a very experimental stage and may prove to be of very little help. Professor Winston is sceptical about how much unexplained infertility may be due to this explanation.

Male Infertility Tests

The standard semen analysis is described in the section about Liz's husband (see p.48). Doctors describe it as 'a less than perfect test despite its being at the centre of the evaluation of male infertility' (editorial in *Journal of Urology*, February 1994). Estimations of what an adequate sperm count should be vary so widely that it has been suggested that each clinic should use the sperm of a man who has recently achieved a pregnancy to compare with the other semen they analyse. An improved test of sperm function would be an invaluable asset to the investigation of infertility.

One of the tests which it was thought might prove to be useful was the Hamster penetration test. This was where the egg of a hamster was mixed with the sperm that was being tested to see if it was penetrated. Despite all the hope for this as an accurate predictor of fertility the results have been so disappointing that it is almost never used today.

A similar test, using the dead eggs from women who have had ovaries removed in hysterectomy, can be more useful. If the sperm penetrate the outer shell of the egg there is no fear of the development of an embryo but it does indicate the healthy response of the sperm.

Why would all efforts not necessarily be made to discover the cause of a couple's infertility?

Diagnosis and treatment of infertility are not always cheap. Within the National Health Service there are sometimes long waiting-lists for treatment. Like any medical condition there cannot be guarantees of successful treatment. It is within this context that arguments about what investigations are necessary take place.

Opinions on necessary investigations vary enormously among individual consultants. A very few clinics have a policy of reserving a certain proportion of their budget for treatment. The result is that not every couple who arrive for their first appointment with infertility problems will be automatically referred for a hysterosalpingogram or a laparoscopy. The thinking behind this is that these tests are often misleading. However, some people come away very disappointed, and with no further understanding of their infertility. But the centres will be able to concentrate on offering IVF to those for whom they think it is most likely to work.

CHAPTER 4

DISAPPOINTMENT AND
RELATIONSHIPS

For some couples, facing infertility brings them closer together but for many it can be an unbearable burden on a relationship. In this chapter some of the women describe the stresses that trying to have children put them under. Many relationships fall apart during the time that infertility is being treated. The huge disappointment after a miscarriage is another enormously difficult trauma to deal with.

Sheila and her husband had now been trying for several years to overcome their infertility problems. Sheila had endometriosis and had taken a drug treatment to try to reduce it. Then she was given superovulatory hormones (Clomid) to try and maximize her chances of conception. Her husband had also had his sperm analysed and, although it was not shown to be the major cause of the infertility, it was thought to be low enough to be a contributing factor. Sheila feels that she was becoming increasingly obsessed with pregnancy.

As time went on, I would just get terribly upset when my periods came on. It was almost like a grieving process for me. There was always this hope beforehand. I remember we went on holiday to Scotland. We had a really lovely time. We hadn't been getting on terribly well because of the pressure of it all, but on this holiday things really improved, and when I got back I thought I was pregnant. We were so excited, but then my period came a week later and it was just devastating. That happened so many times.

The process of planning sex around ovulation got to be a bit much. I wouldn't want to do it other than at the right times because we had to save up the sperm. It sounds really silly out of context, but it becomes so important. I was an expert on sperm at one time you know! I knew about motility and mobility, and how many there should be. I'd always want to have dinner-time conversations with people about sperm, because I'd read everything there was to read about it. But who really wants to know about sperm? It's just that I was constantly thinking about it. Also at the time there was a new operation which was supposed to try and increase the sperm count, but my husband wouldn't go for it because it was still in its early stages. I remember feeling really angry because I was doing all these tests and things but he didn't want to go for anything.

Consciously, the idea had not entered my head that he would be unfaithful. At a subconscious level I must have suspected that something was wrong. It was New Year's day and we were coming back from Sheffield. He said to me, 'I've got to go and see Alison tonight, when we get back.' She was someone he worked with. I immediately burst into tears. And then he said, 'Oh and by the way she's pregnant.' I cried the whole evening even though he hadn't told me at this stage that it was his child. When he came home later that evening he told me that they had had an affair for about four or five months.

I find it hard to explain what a complete shock it was. Even now I don't think I have got over it. Firstly to find out that he had had an affair and secondly that she was pregnant, bearing in mind all the treatment I had been through in the previous months to try to get pregnant.

We went to Relate the following April. By that time I was seriously depressed and instead of reacting I became very introverted. I didn't even get angry towards him. I just behaved as people do who are in deep shock. Now, looking at it from a distance, I can't believe that I didn't get angry. But my grief was so great that I didn't even tell anyone about it. I realize now that he seemed rather callous about the way he told me and that was part of why it was so shocking. I had always thought of him as a really loving, caring person. I find it really hard to come to terms with that side of him. I still don't understand what happened really but he wasn't willing to talk about it. When we went to Relate even the counsellor would become angry with him. He just wanted to continue to believe that it was me who had a problem because I was the one who was depressed. He refused to see that he had contributed to that and that I was quite justifiably depressed. He would suggest that it was just me being neurotic.

He would always say that he didn't want the affair to continue and that he loved me. But he didn't do anything and he wasn't prepared to talk about it. During the time we were having counselling she (Alison) must have left work to go and have the baby, but he would never say anything about it. I became very worried when the time came that her maternity leave ended and they would be back at work together again. I asked him what he was feeling about them being in the same office but again he refused to talk about it.

I never knew her and I have never met her. I used to have dreams about killing her and the baby for years, which was so confusing and deeply shocking. It changed me quite drastically because it made me realize why people do things that are really bizarre. I feel I was sent to the edge of madness almost. I now think, 'There but for the grace of God,' when I see things go badly wrong in other people's lives, because I have had a taste of that.

Even with all this going on I was still overwhelmed by my desire for a child and we were still going to go ahead with the treatment. I find it really hard to describe this to anyone who has never felt that total need. It had completely taken over. I think unless you've been on that cycle then it is really hard to understand it. Nothing else seems as important as that. For me it was a shock because I had never had that urge in my twenties.

Throughout this time the frustration increased because still nothing was happening – sometimes it would seem that I was ovulating, but my cycle was very erratic. My temperature was going up and down so they were convinced I was ovulating with the Clomid. Meanwhile I was having all kinds of internal tests, which was horrid, because I had to leave work all the time. They were trying to find out if there was something in my vaginal fluid that was hostile to the sperm. I hated the fact that I never saw the same person at the hospital. I couldn't feel confident that there was any continuity in the advice I was getting. I also had to go by the maternity ward to get to the infertility clinic. They should never underestimate how hurtful it can be to deal with other women's pregnancies when you can't have children.

When the Clomid wasn't working the doctor said to me, 'You just have to accept that you're not going to have a child.' I remember crying all the way home. Then I went to my GP and told her what he had said to me. I just couldn't accept that I couldn't have a child. At that stage my husband still wanted a child as well. So we decided that it would be worthwhile for me to go for IVF. We were coming to the end of the counselling sessions at Relate, and we were booked in to have the IVF attempt just after Christmas. The doctor was able to give me the drugs on the National Health so I think that was about a reduction of between £300 and £400, but otherwise it was privately paid for. It cost £2,500.

Vivienne had been diagnosed as having pelvic inflammatory disease after she had been fitted with a coil. The doctors had given her several courses of antibiotics to try to combat the infection. The adhesions and damage caused by the infection had resulted in the blocking of her fallopian tubes. Her doctor had wanted to repair some of this damage and to try to make the tube function properly but had decided that the infection was so bad that he couldn't even go ahead with the operation.

I still had a little glimmer of hope that something might happen but after the tubal surgery I was beginning to have irregular periods and I was in constant pain. I had been on painkillers permanently, since the initial problems started, and I was certainly taking them every four to six hours. Looking back, at the time I didn't realize how much pain I was in. One consultant said to me that I was a 'pelvic invalid'. I was fit and well in every other respect but my pelvis was giving me so many problems, I was on an anti-inflammatory antibiotic. But there was still that little bit of me that hoped.

We were posted to Hong Kong in September. I had to get a repeat prescription and needed to arrange to be seen by a new doctor. I went to see a gynaecologist who basically said, 'Don't you think enough's enough?'

The previous consultant I had seen in Germany was trying to let nature take its course. Knowing my personality he knew that the depression was beginning to show. I read my notes, and he had written, 'Under no circumstances, unless it is absolutely essential, is this lady to have a hysterectomy.'

Then I went to Hong Kong and by this time I was really getting a bit upset, because my whole life was beginning to deteriorate. The fact that I wasn't well meant that I wasn't able to go to functions. I was only twenty-eight and should have been having a pretty good social life. The new consultant in Hong Kong thought I should have a hysterectomy. That was in September so I went in and had a hysterectomy.

It was the right decision. In fact I said to the original consultant in Germany who carried out the tubal surgery, 'I'm sorry you didn't just go in and take away all the pain'. He said, 'It's all very well in hindsight but I couldn't take you to theatre with what was supposed to be your last chance of having a child and say I've done a hysterectomy'. Because of the past three years of permanent painkillers, permanent discomfort, all the swelling the pelvic inflammatory disease was causing in my abdomen, I knew that a hysterectomy was a possible outcome. They had warned me to be prepared for it as one possibility.

Much of the problem was caused by the fallopian tubes. They did consider just removing the tubes but by then my uterus was giving me other problems with the irregular periods and more pain. That was why the doctor said to me enough is enough. I knew in my heart of hearts what was going to happen, it was a case of sooner or later.

We talked about the implications of a hysterectomy. I knew that was it. It sounded drastic, but it was the one way that I was going to get rid of the pain and all the hassles that went with it; and obviously yes, it would be the end of any chance of having a child. There had always been that glimmer that perhaps something would filter through and while I had a uterus there was always a chance. I was actually better about the hysterectomy than some of the other surgical procedures. I could see the end result. Physically I didn't look back. I did yoga, I could swim again, I wasn't tired all the time.

I did know about IVF and I was quite interested in it, but in 1982 it was such pioneering surgery. My consultant in Germany became quite excited about the possibility of surrogacy because I have a twin sister. My sister and I discussed it, and she would have done that for me, but I never would have forgiven myself if something had happened to her while she was pregnant. There's always going to be that 1 to 2 per cent chance that she could have an ectopic, or a difficult birth. We thought about it quite fully, but I said no.

There were advantages and disadvantages to being in Hong Kong. I couldn't get home easily, but it was lovely to have the sun. It was quite difficult meeting new people, and not really being properly adjusted. We'd only been out there six weeks so I didn't really have a chance to know a lot of people, but everyone was very kind. I suppose I was quite homesick but I didn't even tell my parents about the hysterectomy until I came out of hospital because I felt it would be a lot for them to cope with.

Nobody would have tried to persuade me against it because there was never any question that it was the right thing to do, because of the pain and the discomfort. I think if there had been any query, I don't think the doctor would have said to me at twenty-eight that this needed to be done. I really think the consultant knew what he was talking about, and I knew the implications. I went two years without any signs of menopause, then I started with the night sweats and mastitis, so I took a hormonal treatment. They had not removed my ovaries.

I was told that if they remove the ovaries the symptoms of menopause will start early, but if you still have your healthy ovaries you will still ovulate. There is a danger that, because the ovaries don't have the fallopian tubes and everything else attached to them, they might atrophy with lack of use. Your cycle is actually diminished. Normally, if they do a hysterectomy and the ovaries are removed, you would need a hormonal replacement. I knew that when you have a hysterectomy, it usually speeds the process of menopause, so that's why they put me on the drug, which I still take. For twelve years I had no more gynaecological problems.

Laura had been through an unnecessarily long process of having a broken coil removed and then some treatment for mild endometriosis. She was becoming impatient and had a strong desire to hurry the doctors along. She and Robert were referred to a private clinic and when they carried out a sperm test it was discovered that Robert's low sperm count was the most likely cause of the infertility.

Robert was then referred to a urologist. They said we should hope for a diagnosis of a varicocoele, which is a varicose vein in the testicles. It supposedly causes a slight temperature increase which kills sperm, but also restricts the number of sperm developing. We felt very optimistic when we were told this was the problem.

Although Robert didn't know that he had a problem before this test he said that he had always suspected something. He and his first wife had been trying to have children for one year. Subsequent to them splitting up she has had several treatments of IVF, and has since adopted. So although he had worried he had put it to the back of his mind; it wasn't as if when they split up she married someone else and had children within a week. Robert said he felt something might be wrong, but didn't know what it was.

He stayed in hospital for two nights and had a general anaesthetic. It was very painful apparently because the surgeon cut into the testicle and it became quite swollen afterwards. Then we had to wait six weeks to find out if there was any difference. The operation did improve things slightly but not enormously.

Surgical correction of a varicose vein in the testicle, a varicocoele, is a fairly simple procedure. The abnormal vessel is either tied or blocked off with a chemical injection. Surgeons argue about the success rate. Some claim a 70 per cent improvement in the sperm count of men treated. Others have stated that after ligation of a varicocoele there is no improvement at all. However, in carefully-selected men, ligation of a varicocoele undoubtedly has a genuinely beneficial effect, with a well-documented improvement in fertility.

So again there was a delay about having sex. But by this time we were at the point where we had accepted that we were again waiting for the results of a test. We had started to think that sex is really about having children. If you've been told to wait six weeks to find out the results there doesn't really seem a lot of point to having sex in between. You just go about your daily routine. I don't think I was ever completely and utterly focused on nothing but children, because I had my own business and there was a lot going on in my life, but I do remember the feeling that time was ticking by.

After problems with severe period pains in her twenties, Rosemary had seen a private gynaecologist in Harley Street who had operated on her in 1979. Several years later, the doctor at Kings who had carried out a laparoscopy had told her he thought there was very little chance that she would be able to have children. Then, miraculously, a few weeks later, she was told by her local GP that a routine pregnancy test was positive. Rosemary and her husband were stunned and completely delighted. They had chosen names for the baby and now planned out their future with the prospect of having at least one child to cherish.

The estimated date of delivery was in April. I'd been pregnant or known I was pregnant for a few weeks. One Saturday David and I had gone for a meal with friends. I went to the loo and noticed that I'd got a discharge. It was not actual bleeding so I wasn't unduly worried. It was dark brown and I showed my friend. She hadn't got any children but she said, 'Well, it's probably OK but if you're going to worry about it perhaps we'd better go to casualty.' So the four of us, she and her husband and David and I, went to the nearest hospital.

I think because I hadn't been pregnant before I was probably a bit naive. I didn't know whether to worry or not. Maybe it was a sixth sense. I can remember being quite nervous on the way to the hospital. I was thinking, 'I hope it is all right, it's got to be all right.'

It was 28 September 1985. We arrived at the hospital early evening. It was obvious as soon as we arrived in casualty that something was going on and it transpired that there was rioting nearby in Brixton. People were coming in with horrific facial wounds and it was quite a nightmarish place. I can remember blood pouring from head wounds and the room was chaos. Sometimes when policemen were brought in with injuries there was cheering. It was absolute mayhem and the staff were obviously rushed off their feet. The tension of the two sides being brought together in casualty was so strong. I just remember finding it really, really frightening and we had to sit there for quite a few hours.

I can remember sitting there thinking, 'Oh, perhaps I shouldn't have come because it seems such a minor thing with all this going on, perhaps I should have left it.' After a long wait – obviously the others took priority – I was taken into a cubicle. I can remember it really clearly; the young doctor came in and he was obviously at the end of his tether with all that was happening. He'd also been on duty for quite some time because he had stubble on his face, he looked absolutely tired and worn out. I could sense that the last thing he needed was a neurotic woman. I felt like that – coming along and saying, 'I'm a bit worried because I'm pregnant and I've got this discharge.' He told me to get up on the couch and he examined me. He said, 'Well, everything seems absolutely fine Mrs Thornton, there's no need to worry and you'll be OK, just go home and rest for a few days.' I felt really relieved, I thought everything was OK.

He left the cubicle and I got down from the couch and stood to get dressed again and just haemorrhaged really, really heavily. My husband was with me. I didn't know what to do but I started shaking because I was so frightened. I said to David, 'I think you'd better go and get the doctor.' David said that he went to try to find the doctor and he was sitting at a desk writing and David asked if he could just come back a moment. He could tell the doctor was quite angry because he threw his pen down. 'Mr Thornton, I've told you your wife is fine.' David insisted he have a look and the doctor came back in to the cubicle and looked down at the floor and I heard him say, 'Oh God, this is all I need.' I can see it from his point of view, he was just at the end of his patience. 'OK, we'll have to admit you – all right?.' From then on I was just so frightened, so terrified that I said to David, 'You won't leave me will you,' and he said, 'Yes, yes of course I'll stay.' They brought a trolley and took me to a ward and by this time it was about eleven o'clock at night. I still thought that everything was going to be all right.

No one said anything about what was wrong. We got to the ward. There was just one light on and it was quiet and the nurse showed me to a bed. She told David he'd have to go. I said, 'I don't want him to go, I want him to stay,' and she said, 'No, it's late, he has to go.' I could see him sort of dithering and he said to me, 'Well, I'll have to go but I'll come back first thing in the morning.' I sat in the chair by the bed.

I sat for quite a while then I went up to the nurses' station. I just said, 'Excuse me, I haven't got any nightie or anything with me at all because I've been admitted from casualty.' One of the nurses tutted and she brought me a sort of loop thing. I was in such a state, I didn't know how to get it on or how to get it round me. I can remember it was really clean but it had holes in and it was faded and it wasn't mine and I just felt it was horrible. I was in this nightie with holes sitting on this bed and I didn't know what to do because I could feel that I was still bleeding. I thought I'd better walk along and go to the loo and I was at one end of this very long ward and the loo was at the other end.

As I went I left a trail of spots of blood going along with me and I went in to the loo and went to the toilet and I lost a lot more blood and I still had no idea what was happening. I was absolutely terrified and shaking like jelly and I just couldn't keep still. I think at one point I thought I must be dying because it seemed to be such a lot of blood. I walked back along the ward to the nurses' station and they were really talking intensely about something and I said, 'Excuse me, I've just been along to the toilet and I've lost a lot of blood and it's gone on to the floor,' and one of the nurses said, 'Well on the shelf up there, there is some paper tissue, you can go along and mop it up.' So I got the tissues down and just went back to retrace my steps and tried to get it up from the floor. Then I went in to the toilet, made sure that that was cleaned up and that I hadn't left a mess.

I got a long strand of toilet paper, and just put that underneath because I didn't have anything like a sanitary towel. I didn't want to have the same thing happen if I went back. I climbed into bed and I just started crying really hysterically because I was so terrified. One of the nurses came over and she said, 'You'll have to be quiet because it's very late and people are trying to sleep and they're ill so you must be quiet.'

She went away and the lady in the bed next to me, who I had probably woken, said, 'What's the matter love?' I said, 'I'm having a baby and I think something's going wrong because I'm bleeding.' She said, 'Oh, you mean sort of a threatened miscarriage.' I hadn't really thought about it in those terms. She said, 'But I've just seen you walking up the ward,' and I said, 'Well I wanted to go to the toilet.' She then told me, 'But you shouldn't be getting out of bed. You should have asked for a bedpan.'

She called one of the nurses over and she said, 'This lady has got a threatened miscarriage and I've just seen her walking up the ward; it's disgusting you should be ashamed and you should be reported.' I don't remember the nurse's reaction but she went off. I can remember feeling really grateful to this lady and thinking, 'I wish I was a bit more like that.' I would have accepted whatever treatment I received because I was in no fit state to question anything. Afterwards, when I told people they said, 'Well, why on earth did you do it when she said to take the paper towel?' But I did it automatically, I didn't think to question it.

It was quite late by then and I didn't sleep and the next morning the nurses started to come round to do the ward rounds. I said to the nurse, 'I think that the bed is wet'. She pulled the bedclothes back and she wrinkled her nose and she had a look of absolute disgust on her face. She said, 'Look at this and the laundry's on strike so I don't know what we're going to do'. There was so much blood in the bed. I had felt it and I knew it was damp but I didn't want to look so I just ignored it really.

Eventually I was taken for a scan. They used terminology like missed abortion. In my mind abortion had a completely different connotation – it was something done by someone who wanted to be rid of their baby. I saw a miscarriage as something completely different, I didn't understand why they used that term. Also I can remember hearing the word 'foetus'. 'Oh, the foetus has just reached six weeks.' That was awful as well because to me it was a baby, it wasn't a foetus, it was my baby. It was medical terminology and it was correct but for me that added to the pain. It was just really upsetting.

I left the hospital on the Tuesday after a D and C. I can remember how I felt then when we were driving away from the hospital and I can remember thinking, 'I've left my baby in that awful place. I can't just drive away and leave it there,'- it was as if I was abandoning it. I thought my mother had abandoned me and now it felt like I was doing the same thing with my baby, that I was just leaving it.

I think David thought that I was crying in the car because of the experience. I don't think I did put it in to words – it just seemed such a ridiculous thing to think. I thought anyone would think it was a completely irrational thing to think because I knew I hadn't left a baby there but that wasn't how it felt.

Miscarriage and stillbirth

Miscarriage is nearly always traumatic and for Rosemary, the feelings of loss and bereavement were not helped by her experience in hospital. Many doctors now recognize that although to them miscarriage is an everyday occurrence, for the woman it is a major disaster and part of the treatment has to be compassion and understanding. The following is a quote from an American journal of postgraduate medicine, published in 1991: 'Miscarriage continues to be an emotionally tormenting event for too many women. Hopefully more investigators will commit themselves to unravelling its yet hidden mysteries.

'Although scientific facts help assuage a couple's fears and apprehension, the critical ingredients in caring for a woman after miscarriage are understanding, sensitivity and compassion. This is the "art" of medicine – something not taught in medical textbooks or by research studies.'

The experience of being in hospital during or after a miscarriage is also made less traumatic by having a basic understanding of the medical terms:

What is a miscarriage and why is it called an abortion?

Women who have had a miscarriage hate to hear it referred to as an abortion. The reason why it happens is because in most medical textbooks, the word abortion is used in both the context of 'spontaneous abortion', meaning miscarriage, and 'induced abortion' meaning termination of pregnancy by choice. Many hospitals, including King's College Hospital where Rosemary was treated, now use the terms 'miscarriage' and 'termination of pregnancy'. It seems to be common sense to use these terms, which reflect the different emotional experiences that the two situations bring with them.

In medical terms abortion simply means the expulsion of a baby before it reaches a stage at which it could survive independently of the mother. In Britain this is considered to be at twenty-four weeks' gestation; in America it is twenty weeks or 500g in weight.

How often does it happen?

It is difficult to come up with a figure for how common miscarriage is because most miscarriages occur at the very early stages of pregnancy and in many cases the woman herself does not know that she is pregnant. More important is how many pregnancies that women are aware of end in miscarriage. This depends on how closely and at what intervals the woman herself and the medical professionals are looking for signs of pregnancy. The most likely figure is now estimated at 18 per cent. Certainly among women who have had several pregnancies it is a common experience to have had a miscarriage; some studies conclude that a quarter of all women will experience a miscarriage at some time.

The likelihood of miscarriage increases as women grow older. The rate in women aged thirty to thirty-four is twice that for women under thirty and in women over thirty-five, three times the rate of under thirty-year-olds. The rate also increases with the number of pregnancies regardless of age: About 6 per cent of first and second pregnancies end in miscarriage, but it increases to 16 per cent with subsequent pregnancies.

At least 90 per cent of miscarriages happen before the pregnancy reaches sixteen weeks and the vast majority of these happen before twelve weeks. This is why all the books suggest you wait until twelve weeks before telling people you are pregnant.

What are the different types of miscarriage?

Discovering that you are bleeding in the early weeks of pregnancy is very alarming and you should tell your doctor immediately. It does not necessarily mean you will lose the baby. The most common cause of vaginal bleeding in early pregnancy is one of the forms of miscarriage. Vaginal bleeding in the first twenty-four weeks of a pregnancy is a recognized reason for emergency admission to hospital. So going to casualty would be perfectly reasonable. These are the symptoms of the different types of miscarriage which a doctor or midwife will be looking for:

What is a threatened miscarriage (abortion)?

Bleeding from inside the uterus before the twenty-fourth week of pregnancy, without the cervix being dilated. This type of bleeding is rarely heavy and seldom requires tranfusion. Some women bleed slightly at the time they would have expected their first period; this is called an implantation haemorrhage and is not a sign of an impending miscarriage.

Threatened miscarriage happens in about 10 per cent of all pregnancies. Usually the medical person will do an internal examination, perhaps using a speculum and probably an ultrasound scan. If the ultrasound reveals a live foetus – the heart can be seen pulsating after about seven weeks – and an absence of other abnormalities, the pregnancy will continue in 95 per cent of cases and the woman will be reassured.

Traditionally women with the symptoms of a threatened miscarriage are advised to go to bed and rest. There is no scientific evidence that this actually stops a miscarriage but simply having the feeling that you can do something to help may be therapeutic. At the moment there don't seem to be any specific treatments for threatened miscarriage.

What do they mean by an inevitable miscarriage (abortion)?

A miscarriage is called inevitable if – in addition to bleeding – strong and painful uterine contractions occur which cause the cervix to dilate. This will be assessed by a vaginal examination. An inevitable miscarriage may develop from a threatened miscarriage but is more likely to occur without any warning. The miscarriage occurs frequently quite soon after the symptoms begin and results in a complete or incomplete miscarriage. If the woman is not in hospital when this is diagnosed, the doctor or midwife will want to transfer her to hospital as soon as possible.

What is the difference between a complete and incomplete miscarriage?

Complete miscarriage (abortion)

When a baby is conceived the uterus will contain the foetus, the membrane which holds the amniotic fluid, and the placenta (the blood supply). In a complete miscarriage all of this is forced out of the uterus by contractions, in the form of blood, clots and tissue. The pain then usually ceases but spotting (slight bleeding) may persist for about ten days afterwards. Most miscarriages will be assumed to be incomplete.

Incomplete miscarriage (abortion)

This is more common and a bit more dangerous and it can, very rarely, result in heavy bleeding and shock. Because not all the products of a conception have been expelled from the uterus heavy bleeding may persist, especially if the remnants of the placenta are left – this was the blood supply for the foetus. Once the clots and or tissue have been expelled any pain in the lower abdomen is usually dramatically relieved, and pain afterwards is very uncommon. Emergency treatment may include the use of oxytocic drugs, which cause the uterus to contract and therefore help to stop the bleeding. In some cases the woman will have to have a drip for intravenous fluids or a blood transfusion.

Once the woman's condition is stable, the remnants left in the uterus have to be removed. This will be done during a D and C – dilatation and curettage.

What is a missed abortion (miscarriage)?

In a few cases, the dead foetus, membranes and placenta, are not expelled spontaneously by the uterus, i.e. there is no evidence that the death has taken place. Usually the woman will then have a delayed period which may be a bit heavier than usual, but what has happened is that the baby has died but just remains inside. The symptoms of pregnancy disappear and the uterus stops growing – it may even decrease in size. Some women with a missed abortion will have an intermittent brown discharge.

Treatment is not as urgent as an incomplete miscarriage and many missed abortions result in a miscarriage in the end. If it is detected and no miscarriage takes place some women will be advised to have a D and C.

What happens when the miscarriage is infected?

Septic miscarriage/abortion

These are complications in which a spontaneous miscarriage is associated with an infection of the genital organs. It becomes a septic miscarriage if the infection is passed into the woman's bloodstream.

The other terms used in medicine are early and late abortion (miscarriage). This refers to whether it is in the first trimester (twelve weeks) or second (up to twenty-four). The loss of a baby after this would be referred to as stillbirth.

Habitual Miscarriage (abortion)

Many women find it distressing that doctors may sometimes only investigate the cause of miscarriage if she has suffered three miscarriages in a row. This decision depends on the type of miscarriage and other circumstances. A distinction is made between women who have three consecutive miscarriages and others because most miscarriages are simply the loss of a foetus which could not have survived, because of genetic abnormality. The chance of this happening more than once is low. The Cambridge Early Pregnancy Loss Study suggests that women in their first pregnancy and women whose last pregnancy was successful run only a 5 per cent risk of miscarriage, whereas women with one, two or three previous miscarriages run a risk of 20 per cent, 28 per cent and 43 per cent, respectively, of miscarrying their next pregnancy.

How should miscarriage be managed by medical staff?

Since the time when Rosemary suffered her miscarriage there have been many recommendations made for the better management of the situation by medical staff. The anxiety which is caused by any miscarriage should be expected and responded to and every pregnant woman complaining of blood loss in the first twenty-four weeks of pregnancy should be seen as an emergency.

'Grief can be very intense. The miscarriage comes as a shattering blow to most patients, who rarely appreciate how common the problem is in early pregnancy. It is usually not sufficient to explain that one in six pregnancies ends in miscarriage and that this is nature's defence against abnormal conceptions. Feelings of anger and bewilderment frequently develop when the patient finds there is no obvious explanation for the miscarriage and no treatment available to guarantee future success.'

The whole physical experience of miscarriage – such as cramping, bleeding and the passage of tissue – can be frightening. Women sometimes fear that they will bleed to death. This is extremely rare and once the placental tissue has been passed serious bleeding stops.

The physical suffering is often intense but usually short-lived. But the emotional aftermath sometimes stays with women all their lives. It is impossible not to be disappointed, having thought about the possibility of a child. Many people, both relatives and medical staff, say things like, 'Oh you're young. You will have other babies.' For a recently bereaved mother this is enormously upsetting because at that moment she is thinking only about the child she has just lost. To her it would seem like a betrayal of that child to start to try and console herself with the thought of other children.

Marie Lamb, the founder of an American organization called SHARE, has described women who miscarry as 'caught in an emotional grey area between the ongoing frustration of infertility and the pain of losing a beloved child. To mourn the loss is agonizing; to forget about it seems like betrayal.'

The initial shock is followed by more difficult emotions. Many women go through a frantic search for a cause. In the absence of any satisfactory medical explanation they end up pointing the finger at themselves. 'Why didn't I start taking vitamins, or maybe it was the cold remedy. If only I hadn't gone swimming; was it because I had sex?'

These feelings are often reinforced by myth. Some of the modern day ideas are that miscarriages are caused by marital conflicts, fear or neuroses, and still people believe such things as that it might cause the baby to die if a mother lifts something which is too heavy.

However, the situation in most hospitals remains that for busy medical staff, miscarriage is an everyday occurrence. Many women still feel bitter about being rushed in and out of operating theatres and given little explanation or opportunity to ask questions. Doctors' and nurses' well-meaning attempts to discharge the mother early can sometimes be interpreted by the patient as no one caring.

Not all hospitals routinely follow up patients who have had miscarriages and so it is often the GP who has to try and counsel distressed couples. The Miscarriage Association is a very well-run organization and many women have found it incredibly helpful to speak to someone who has gone through the same experience.

Doctors give differing advice about when to attempt another pregnancy but it is probably different for each woman. If a woman has not mourned the loss of her child, even a successful pregnancy will not console her and she may still suffer the symptoms of bereavement. Some hospitals offer bereavement counselling so it is worth asking about this.

Eventually the question, 'Will it happen again?' needs to be answered. The prospects of having a normal healthy baby are excellent. 95 per cent of women who have early miscarriages conceive again within two years. Of these, 79 per cent deliver their babies at the normal time (after thirty-seven weeks' gestation).

Miscarriage is often very difficult for fathers. Many men are confused by the depth of their partner's sorrow. Often their attempts to comfort their partners fall flat. The woman starts to feel that not even he understands how she feels. Inevitably what everyone needs is hope. Over the years there has been a great deal of research into the causes of miscarriage – particularly habitual miscarriage. Many may find comfort in understanding the underlying causes. The Miscarriage Association can offer advice on useful books and information.

CHAPTER 5

ASSISTED REPRODUCTIVE TECHNOLOGY

The first 'test-tube' baby, Louise Brown, was born in 1978. Her birth was greeted as a great breakthrough in the treatment of infertility. Since then in vitro fertilization and embryo transfer have brought hope and even babies to many previously infertile couples. However, it should be remembered that IVF is not suitable for many people and the success and failure rates at the end of this chapter make sobering reading.

In this chapter Miranda gives a very detailed description of the process which led up to her IVF attempts. Then the other women describe their various attempts at IVF, microsurgery and GIFT.

Miranda had been referred to the Hammersmith Hospital Infertility Clinic. The staff had carried out a hysterosalpingogram, a laparoscopy, sperm and mucus tests, a post-coital test and had monitored two of Miranda's menstrual cycles. These tests were done not only with the intention of finding the right diagnosis, but also to see if Clive and Miranda would be suitable patients for further fertility treatments, including IVF. The main problem seemed to be that she had polycystic ovaries.

Before trying the full IVF treatment the consultant wanted to try Clomid in three cycles, because that's the easiest and cheapest treatment for everyone. It's cheapest in terms of effort and it often works for people with polycystic ovaries. The first month I took it my period was a little late, and I did wonder if I had perhaps conceived briefly, but I never knew. Clomid didn't solve the problems I had with the luteinizing hormone (*the hormone which stimulates the ovaries to release the egg*), but it was worth a try. I was told that for all women, Clomid suppresses oestrogen, but for some, like me, it suppresses it to a point where you couldn't conceive. This is because the lack of oestrogen affects the cervical mucus and the sperm need cervical mucus to survive. Because it had this effect on me I only did two out of three proposed cycles.

Clomid or Serophene – These are the commercial names for Clomiphene, which is the most commonly used fertility pill. Clomiphene is an anti-oestrogen which has few side-effects. Ironically, it was first investigated as an alternative to the contraceptive pill because of this. It promotes ovulation by stimulating the natural release of FSH (follicle-stimulating hormone) from the pituitary gland. This is the hormone that makes the ovaries work harder to produce follicles which will mature eggs. One of its advantages over other hormonal treatments is that it rarely causes multiple births because it is only a weak stimulant. However, it is still the commonest cause of multiple birth in the UK.

One of the less beneficial effects of low oestrogen is a thickening of the cervical mucus, making the cervix unresponsive to the sperm. In some women it also interferes with the uterine lining, which may make it more difficult for an embryo to implant.

Clomiphene has been a very important and successful treatment for women who have problems with ovulation.

So then I was booked in for an assisted cycle. It's the same drugs as IVF but you don't have the operation to collect the eggs and they are not fertilized in laboratory conditions.

It wasn't my next menstrual cycle. There was a delay, because you have to be booked in and the clinic is always busy. Even though I felt an urgency it was always a relief to go away for a bit. I was still hoping that maybe I wouldn't need to come back and maybe I'd get pregnant without help.

During an assisted cycle the doctors go through the process of taking over the woman's ovulation cycle with hormonal drugs. In this way they hope to control the production of several eggs but they avoid going to all the inconvenience and expense of removing the eggs and fertilizing them in laboratory conditions. Instead they inseminate the woman with sperm at the optimum time for conception.

I first went to see a consultant in 1991, so it's been two and a half years and I have been through two assisted cycles with intra-uterine insemination and three IVF attempts. Many women wait much longer than I have. When I meet other women in my situation, I realize it's a combination of fortune and determination to go to the right place first.

I hate to imagine how much more traumatic it could have been to be shuffled about for years on end – thank God it was only months.

The first thing that happens on an assisted cycle is the suspension of your normal cycle. This is done by sniffing Buserelin. You have a little bottle of it, and you have to absorb it through the membranes of your nose. It suppresses the pituitary gland. I was very anxious about this. I was worried about taking very powerful drugs and what it might do to me. So I had to overcome a lot of fear.

I was wary of drugs in general and I was also worried about these particular drugs. I had read about them. I was afraid of what it might do in the long term. I was just driven by such a need to have a child that I was prepared to take the risk. Although there were times when I really wondered if it was right to take this step.

Buserelin is a drug which suppresses the hormone production of the pituitary gland. It comes in the form of a nasal spray. This has to be sniffed every four hours during the day and then last thing at night as well as first thing in the morning. The pituitary gland normally produces two hormones, which are part of the cycle, that stimulate the ovaries to produce eggs. By suppressing these hormones doctors cause the woman to stop menstruating, ironically for someone who is trying to get pregnant. After two and a half weeks the ovaries are suppressed and then the doctors stimulate ovulation by injections of particular hormones. Given this more controlled ovulation cycle the eggs are more likely to be collected at the optimum moment for fertilization.

I sniffed Buserelin for about two and a half weeks. It was all very well organized. I always went in on a Tuesday at least two and a half weeks after I started sniffing. I had a scan to see if my ovaries were suppressed. There was also a blood test to confirm that my hormones had dropped away to nothing. Then I received the call to say everything was okay and I could start the stimulating hormone injections.

The next stage of the treatment is to mimic the body's production of hormones. First the ovaries are stimulated to start producing eggs, then when the eggs are fully mature another hormone, which stimulates the release of the eggs, is introduced.

I had to have all the second phase of drugs ready. I had asked my GP to prescribe them for me, otherwise I would have had to buy them. Some women are unfortunate that their GPs won't prescribe it for them. I was lucky that the NHS paid for it.

At the same time that I started these drugs I also started going in for scans and blood tests at regular times, and they monitored very carefully how many follicles had been stimulated and how they were growing. The first time I had seventeen days of injections which made my ovaries develop the eggs to a point where they were ripe for release. I got very tired and sore.

Pergonal is a drug they used to get from menopausal women. I remember reading that it is collected from the urine of Catholic nuns in Italy. Menopausal women have large amounts of follicle-stimulating hormone in their blood naturally. They use nun's urine because convents have large groups of menopausal women all in one place. It is ironic because the Catholic Church is opposed to IVF treatment. I found it a comforting thought that women's bodies produce this hormone to try to overcome a natural ageing effect. At that stage in your life you are producing more and more of the hormone, which reassured me that having a lot of follicle-stimulating hormone in my blood when I was being over-stimulated was not as worrying or unnatural as it might have been.

When I had the assisted cycle they only wanted one or two of my follicles to come to fruition so they kept the dose quite low. The first time was partly an experiment to see how my body would respond. People with polycystic ovaries respond variably, so you have to be very careful. I've often wondered if it has been the effect of homeopathy that I have responded more or less the same way every time: very smoothly without any kind of panics. I responded very well to all of the treatments. They tell you to come back for the final injection, HGC (luteinizing hormone), which is the last surge to bring about ovulation. You ovulate within thirty-six hours of that.

The stimulation of the ovaries is started with HMG – human menopausal gonadotrophin (the commercial names are Pergonal or Humegon) – which is given by injection. The follicles of the ovary are then monitored both by regular blood tests for hormonal information and by ultrasound. Vaginal ultrasound is more effective for this type of scanning and much more convenient for the woman. If the ultrasound scan is from outside the abdomen the woman's bladder has to be full.

In a cycle like Miranda's, where the natural production of hormones has been suspended, another hormone has to be injected. Just at the point when the other tests show that the eggs have reached the optimum point of maturity, HCG (human chorionic gonadotrophin) will be given. This sends a message to the ovary to start the process by which the follicle ruptures and ovulation itself happens. Normally ovulation will occur about thirty-seven hours after the injection and egg collection must be done before this time has elapsed. The injection of HCG also initiates a chemical process within the egg which ripens it before a woman ovulates.

You would think that because you are so aware of all this going on in your body you might be able to feel it. I couldn't, though I know women who feel they are aware of ovulation happening.

The first two assisted cycles we did not go as far as IVF. Instead we tried intra-uterine insemination (IUI). Clive gave a sperm sample, and they washed it and put it up high in my uterus. This seems to help, even when the sperm are very healthy. It seems to help statistically. We opted to try both the IUI and making love naturally as well.

I had two assisted cycles with IUI. I was frustrated with it because I was doing all the sniffing and injections yet not actually achieving anything. I thought why not do IVF, and go all the way. It seems like two-thirds of the pain and aggravation, because you're not sure if you've really ovulated, or if the egg was OK. I was left feeling I hadn't really found anything out. I'm not sure that was terribly rational but that was how I felt.

All I knew was that I wasn't pregnant. I didn't know if I was actually ovulating, if my eggs were of a good quality, or if I was capable of making an embryo with Clive. It was ironic because I nearly didn't go through with the third assisted cycle. I wanted to go straight to IVF. I talked it through with the consultant and with Clive. Then we agreed to give it one more go. That time they put me on a higher dose of Pergonal to start. I started on two instead of one and a half. I just went like a train, and by day nine when they did the scan, I didn't have to be told, I could see myself there was no way I could do as before because I had follicles busting out all over. I had to either cancel the cycle or do IVF. I was shocked but I didn't really hesitate. That was on a Friday, and on the Monday I was in the hospital having an egg collection.

Egg collection is an operation to take the mature eggs from the ovaries so that they can be mixed with sperm outside the body. 'In vitro' literally means in glass.

I've had two very different experiences of egg collection. The first time I was very nervous because I didn't know what to expect, but I didn't feel a thing. I went into the theatre and lay down. Then the anaesthetist gave me painkillers and tranquillizers through the back of my hand. Actually, I slept through most of it, snored apparently and was high as a kite for twenty-four hours. One of the good things about it was that partners can come in, so Clive was there. I was also euphoric because it's all so novel and exciting. They got sixteen eggs out, which was pretty good. Then I went away and rested for forty-eight hours, and then back to the hospital again.

I remember feeling thrilled because it seemed a bit heroic in a way, in the sense that I was actually doing something. I got swept along in the enthusiasm of all these people rushing about, and there I was, there were my eggs: they count them up, and there were sixteen. That was one of the frustrations with the previous assisted cycles – because I ended up having achieved nothing. IVF generates its own excitement. I just felt as though each step I was getting somewhere.

After the egg collection the staff in the laboratory put Clive's sperm with my eggs. They called us back to the hospital, and reported back about the status of our eggs and how many had been fertilized. Then we discussed together with the doctors how many to put back in. They only put two back in for me, because with my age and health I had a very high risk of having every embryo implant.

For the first IVF I was thirty-one, which is young in the IVF game. I had eleven fertilized, so there were lots to choose from, and there were several of good quality. So they put two back in that they said were of very good quality. We saw a picture of our embryos on a printout.

Then they put them back into my uterus using a speculum and inserting a tube through my cervix. I lay down for half an hour, which is more superstition than anything, just for things to settle. Then I was given a load of progesterone injections: two that first day of transfer, one in theatre and one in the evening. Then three the next day and three the day after that. This is just the Hammersmith regime. Other places have different regimes.

It's up to you how you organize the giving of injections. The first time I was in and out of the GP's, because my GP has been completely supportive throughout the treatment. After the course of injections you just wait.

As you can imagine life starts to be run around the treatment schedule. I was obsessed. I can't imagine how you could work – I just more or less gave up. I was exhausted and had to go to bed every afternoon to sleep. I just find it emotionally and physically exhausting. I think most women have to give up work or work gives them up.

At that time I was giving blood on days ten, twelve and fourteen. I went and got the blood taken on days ten and twelve and took it into the hospital on day fourteen when they did the final pregnancy test. They ring you later that day, if it's the test day or the following day. I was really hopeful because they had told me the embryos were such good quality. I was so buoyed along by this tide. When we hadn't heard Clive went down (because he works there) to the clinic and found out I definitely wasn't pregnant. I was devastated. I just withdrew.

When Clive phoned my mother was with me and a close friend. They were very distressed because they just didn't know how to help me at all. I just wouldn't let them. I froze. I'm sometimes like that when I'm really distressed. I don't cry or throw things about, and I think people around me find that terribly difficult. I just shut off and I didn't start crying for hours and hours. I was then shattered and had to spend a couple of days in bed. I was broken.

I actually find this distressing to talk about. It was the most intense grieving I've ever done. The following morning my mother said she had to go back home – I didn't want her to go, but she absolutely had to. I took her to the local station and on the way home I just cried. I cried my eyes out on the street and made a complete exhibition of myself. A man actually came up and asked me if I was OK. I had run out of any emotional resources I'd ever had.

I was just despairing that I'd ever be a mother; I felt that I just couldn't do it. I was desperate at the thought that I would keep on trying and trying and ruin my life by trying, and that I'd never, never have a baby. It was a very generalized despair. I'd felt that before in many ways but this time I just collapsed. For a few days I just fell down under the grief. I couldn't speak to people on the phone. I could hardly get out of bed. In retrospect it lasted a relatively short while. It was probably the right thing to do, to collapse completely. I couldn't have done anything else really.

For Clive, it was different – much more specifically to do with these lost babies. He found the sight of embryos hugely moving. It really distressed him. I don't know if it's him or if it's men in general; but it's more visual. For him it was so intensely moving and distressing to have seen the embryos and for them not to have survived, whereas for me it was just a generalized thing. It wouldn't have mattered if I had seen a picture of them or not really.

I decided then to give in and to just drift for a few weeks and be very gentle with myself. I've never been alone with this problem. I have always had support from people around me. I am that type of person, which I'm sure makes it easier to cope with these kinds of failures. I'm sensible enough to have these people around me. I seek support and they give it. So I don't fall to pieces and stay in pieces. Homeopathy really helped me and although it never cured my infertility it has treated my despair.

Even at my lowest I think I was pretty sure I would try again. I wasn't exactly using the thought to try and comfort myself by rekindling hope. And people who were close to me were sensible enough not to say, 'it will be all right next time'. I had to hammer it into some of them that it might not ever work out. The people who were really close to me educated themselves, so that they would come to understand what was going on. They understood that there was hope but not enough to say that it would be fine next time.

There is no doubt that you come to know and accept yourself at times like this. My own personality has a side that is very despairing. But that is me. That's how I respond to things, or it can be. I also have another side that is hopeful. If you didn't have hope you wouldn't do the treatment. It's always mixed. It's always been two sides of the same coin for me. I know some women think they'll keep going until they have a baby. They won't allow themselves to think it might not work next time.

I think it's probably essential really to grieve. It is like a bereavement; like somebody's died. When you can't have children it's like somebody dies over and over again. If you bottle grief up you're not ever free of it. I don't regret grieving. I knew I was going to do IVF again, because everyone told me it was worth doing it three times. Some people say it's worth doing more than that. In the *Prospect* newsletter from Hammersmith support group, I've just read that someone had a son on their sixth IVF attempt. Obviously they found the strength from somewhere to do it six times.

I saw the consultant after the failed IVF. In his view there was hope. He said that physically I responded very well, and I did very well. He said that IVF would probably work for me but that it might not be the second time or the tenth time. It was a very good thing to say because it's so realistic. Then you have to go away and think about whether you've got the physical and emotional strength and whether you've got the money to do it. He said I had a really good chance.

I don't cry when I'm with the doctors and nurses. It's part of my strategy for coping. I want to befriend them in a way. I want to be an easy patient so that I get the best out of the situation. It sounds sort of cynical, but I feel a bit more in control of the situation if I'm positive with them, and I'm getting that back I suppose.

After taking a hormonal drug treatment for endometriosis and then a course of drugs to stimulate ovulation, Sheila had still not become pregnant. Her marriage was under a great deal of strain. The woman her husband had had an affair with had by now had his child. But he and Sheila were still together and she was determined to go through with an attempt at IVF.

During the treatment I had to travel thirty-five miles on the train to the clinic every day. I also remember having to collect urine samples at work so I had to carry these little bottles around with me. It was all really horrid. One of the things I found most upsetting was that I couldn't talk about it at work. It's just not the sort of thing you can talk about. It was such a major thing going on in my life yet I just had to pretend that nothing was happening.

It was really hard. It is such a personal thing and it involves personal details about your body. I don't know whether another kind of person would have been able to talk about it. But then I've not met anybody who does talk about it. That makes me think that it's not just me blaming myself.

I was full of anger at the time. I felt really lonely because I was travelling back to London every day to this hostel and having to wait in this clinic. I just found it a horrid experience. I was paying so much money, something like £2500. Each time I went I would sit in a waiting room full of people I didn't know. Every day the clinic seemed to be full of different people. There wasn't a warm friendly atmosphere. I just had no relationship with anybody, so it was really hard, there was nothing to latch on to.

I took the drugs which are given to stimulate the ovulation process and by the middle of the cycle they checked to see if the eggs were mature. There were no eggs, I hadn't even ovulated. I was given the option of trying again but by this time I just knew I could not go through it again.

I was devastated. At that point I was starting to recognize that my marriage wasn't going to continue. I came home from the clinic on a really, really cold winter's day in December. My husband was at a college course that day, and I rang him to say that it had failed. I thought he'd come home straightaway, but he didn't. It was then that I knew that I didn't actually have any support. So that was really difficult.

It seems a bit crazy in retrospect. He had told me the affair was over and I wanted it not to make a difference. I obviously wasn't facing up to things. I was so focused on becoming pregnant that I was willing to ignore anything which might divert from that course. The affair interrupted it but it couldn't stop the process. I had to continue because I'd already started.

After the IVF attempt failed I realized how much it had cost me emotionally and physically, and of course financially. I finally saw there had to be a point where I made a decision to stop.

I still wanted the marriage. I thought, okay we can't have children, there are other exciting things we can do with our lives. I wanted to go travelling. I realized that major changes needed to take place in my life. I was working in a college and after the IVF failed I gave in my notice. I felt I had to review everything.

So we went to South America for seven weeks. That definitely finished our marriage completely. Things went from bad to worse within a very short period of time. It was a very challenging situation. By that time there wasn't enough substance to the relationship. I think he found it difficult and I did as well. Going to a Third World country, and not having been before, was quite a shock, on top of what we'd been through over the last couple of years.

It was a classic mistake. I learned so much from that journey. I'd thought, I'll go to the other side of the world, get away from all this, open new horizons – and of course you take what you're trying to get away from with you.

I have never been able truly to sort out in my mind what exactly happened to my marriage. The reason I married him was that he was a caring, loving person. I just think that the things that happened to us were too much for him to handle; the uncertainty just made him put his head in the sand. He used to pretend the uncertainty wasn't there. I got depressed and in need of his reassurance, and the more depressed I got the angrier he got with me, so it was just a vicious circle.

L aura's doctor recommended IVF treatment. She had three attempts at IVF. The first attempt was in July 1988, the second was in October 1988, and the third attempt was in January 1989.

As far as the drugs were concerned – I don't remember worrying about them. The only thing that panicked me was when I was running low and I had to phone my local GP and ask if he would prescribe the drugs. They were great about it. The only drug I had to buy individually was the one you need at midnight. (*The drug which stimulates the ovaries to release the egg.*) You had to take it thirty-six hours before the operation.

I was in quite a fortunate position about work because I am self-employed. I have a very good friend who's a nurse, and my brother-in-law and father-in-law are doctors, so for the attempt which fell over the Christmas holidays I just took all the drugs down with me and every day one of them would give me the injections.

I didn't really find it a hassle or painful. I think there is something quite involving about it. You feel like you're at last on the road to getting pregnant. I remember having the attitude that 'If this is what it takes I'll just get on with it.' I have very little time for complaints like, 'Oh God, you have to go every day for injections.' I always brushed it off, but maybe that's my way of dealing with it. I just thought, well, at least I'm on the way and at the end of it I might be pregnant and that would be brilliant. Also, once I'd had the injections for eight days, I started going in for scans and I could see my ovaries growing these follicles. My pregnant friends had scans so I felt great about that.

The thing with me was that because I had so many eggs every time – the dose stimulated a lot of follicles – I seemed to be getting back a lot for my effort. Instead of just taking two weeks to hatch, I'd be having twenty-one days of injections to get them all up to the leading follicle being 2cm in size. That was a bit of a problem because it was only supposed to be two weeks of injections.

I felt completely accepting about giving up work. Now I think it would be quite difficult. In those days I was busy and had the odd job but I wasn't working nearly as much as I am now. I'm fairly committed and quite busy and having to say no to clients would be difficult. I didn't find it a problem; I thought that's what you have to do to have a child.

Psychologically, it didn't seem to affect me as badly as it does some women. I think the reason it didn't was because the major cause of our infertility was not in fact me. I think that's the easiest balance, if you have to have it any way, better that the man has the problem. There's nothing worse than the stench of a burning martyr.

The first time, I didn't tell anyone I was having treatment. I didn't want everyone asking me about all the drugs I had to take, and how awful it was. The second time I realized that was a bit crazy. It's like not telling people you're pregnant until you're twelve weeks pregnant in case you miscarry – in actual fact if you do miscarry you're going to tell people you've had a miscarriage. The second time I actually needed help with the injections on weekends. People have been enormously supportive. Each time I found myself looking forward to the next time I was going to have it done.

The leading follicle was at 2cm, so I went to have the HCG injection at midnight (*the hormone which stimulates the follicles to rupture and finally release the mature eggs*). Then thirty-six hours later, which was about ten in the morning, Robert came with me to provide the sperm. He didn't seem to find it too embarrassing and by the end he had had to do it about four times so he was getting used to it. I think we sort of shielded each other from what we were actually thinking about. We were pretty optimistic and buoyant, and it was all terribly exciting.

Then came the general anaesthetic, which I hated. That's actually one thing I loathe. I hate coming round from it as well as the injections beforehand. I've heard of people who just sit still and have the egg collection done under a local anaesthetic; I don't know how they can do that; I just think it would be awful.

I don't remember feeling particularly sensitive about it being invasive. The funny thing is that you don't really have that many internal examinations that you're aware of. The scan was done externally. So, I didn't really mind. You feel each step is on the way to getting pregnant. Even when I was being prepared for the general I was lying on a bed, but my feet weren't up in stirrups. It was a lot more dignified than it could have been.

After the first egg collection I stayed in the hospital overnight. I was incredibly excited and convinced I was going to be pregnant. They had replaced two eggs and sperm into my uterus. Of the sixteen eggs removed four were taken and twelve were frozen for further attempts. Two were placed in a test-tube to see if they would fertilize. The next morning I found out that the eggs that were in the test-tube had failed to fertilize, so there was very little chance of a pregnancy. I told them if they wanted to use them for research they could. I was still hoping that a miracle would happen . . . then the second attempt was virtually the same.

Well, we went away on holiday in August, and the specialist said he'd prefer me to have two natural periods before we had another go. We were on holiday with Robert's sister and brother-in-law and their three children. I don't remember being really depressed about it. We just sort of focused on the next attempt really. I didn't particularly start to doubt the treatment either.

After the second attempt I began to get a bit pissed off. I started to think we were three grand down. The eggs which were collected that time were tested with donor sperm and they all fertilized. So my eggs were absolutely fine. Most women produce six eggs or eight eggs – I was producing sixteen or eighteen. We could have gone on trying with six attempts every year and nothing happening.

After the first attempt we thought of the possibility of a donor. When the second attempt failed we had to think about it very seriously. Robert said, 'There comes a point when we can't keep taking eggs out.' In the end it was a joint decision because it was really the only option.

There was an enormous conflict in the beginning. Robert initially wanted to try adopting. I started getting very angry. I said, 'Why should we adopt?' We were both getting too old to adopt and we didn't look like good parents because we are both self-employed. I think the children are never really yours and I'm too young to think about doing it to be kind. I said, 'Let's face it, we are not going to be able to adopt and we are going to be childless.' The bad time lasted for about two weeks and then the decision just came by itself. It wasn't a difficult decision for me, but I think it was a difficult decision for Robert. Having taken it, however, there was no looking back.

Given this conflict, it was strange that on the third attempt I think he was a lot closer to me. And the conflict has never come up again. In fact we very rarely talk about it between ourselves – not because it's a forbidden subject or a difficult subject – it really is a completely irrelevant subject. When someone else brings it up out of the blue I just say, 'I don't really want to talk about it.' I think it's a very personal thing for Robert and I want to protect him. I am extremely grateful to him because for some men it's a completely impossible decision to make.

Rosemary's miscarriage had been extremely traumatic. Both she and her husband David were finding it hard to communicate their grief to each other. Rosemary was trapped between the feeling of desperation for a child and the terrible fear which pregnancy now brought with it.

I think the experience of hospital had a tremendous impact. I would have been devastated and upset anyway. I had been told I didn't have a chance of having this baby and then I was so happy when I found out I was pregnant. I would have been devastated whatever. But it would have been easier if the hospital experience had been more sympathetic. It has stayed with me. I had nightmares for years afterwards.

I would dream of being in the bed and being totally isolated and alone, of not being able to make a noise, and of lying in a pool of blood. I would wake up sweating and I was so relieved that it was a nightmare and it wasn't real. These nightmares would occur particularly around the times I underwent infertility treatment – when I was thinking about trying to become pregnant again. I used to think, 'If the treatment does work and I become pregnant it might lead to that kind of experience again.' It was hard not to be ambivalent.

It was also hard to communicate what I felt even to David. I think I could feel my emotions boiling up inside, really boiling and I think after a while, after maybe three or four weeks the main emotion I felt was absolute anger. It wasn't something I shared with David, I think it was something I vented against him, mostly because he was the only person there.

I can remember one Saturday morning I got up and the anger was so great I didn't know what to do with it. I felt at that time that David's attitude was 'Well, now we've had three or four weeks and you should start trying to get yourself together.' I knew he was not unkind but I felt he was expecting me to pull myself together and try to get over it. I still had so much emotion left.

That Saturday morning he appeared to be fine and I resented that and

I can remember we had a blazing row. I said that he just didn't understand and he didn't care. I said he had no idea how much it had meant to me and that I couldn't just pull myself together and be OK. Then I said, 'I'm not staying here with you today, I'm taking myself off and I'm going to the sea, I'm going to Brighton or somewhere like that. You can do what you want to do,' and I stormed out of the house.

I went to the station and sat there, trying to calm down. I was shaking with anger – I was about to erupt. I just couldn't seem to control it. David turned up after a while. I saw him buy a ticket and didn't try to stop him although I knew I wasn't going to go to Brighton.

We went to a cafe in Richmond. It was busy but there was a fairly calm sort of atmosphere, people were chatting quietly but it wasn't a noisy place at all. David said something quite innocent and that was it. I can just remember banging and shouting. I am someone who doesn't swear, if I did it would be a mild expletive like bloody. This particular morning I was enraged: 'I'm effing-well fed up with this, I'm effing-well fed up with you and I'm effing fed up with the lot of you and I'm sick to death of no one effing-well understanding.'

I can remember David sitting there. He was really, really embarrassed and I didn't care and I could see people looking as they do and I can remember looking up and saying, 'I don't effing-well care who effing hears me because I am so effing sick of it.' The words poured out of me.

We drove into the countryside and we just sat and talked. He asked me why I had behaved so badly and he was very ashamed and very embarrassed. I said that was tough because he had to realize how I felt. I felt not only had I carried all the physically unpleasant side of it, I was now left to deal with all the emotion and he'd seemed to have got away very lightly in my opinion. I felt the least he could do was to try and understand what I was trying to do.

It was some time before Rosemary felt she wanted to try and conceive again. She was eventually referred to Mrs Varma at St George's Hospital in Wandsworth. Mrs Varma had carried out another laparoscopy and was keen to try microsurgery on Rosemary's one remaining fallopian tube in order to see if she would then conceive.

I was so pleased to have Mrs Varma as my consultant. I think she took my emotions on board a lot more than the other doctors I'd had. She always shared – when I came in for the scan and I was pregnant, she was very happy, she was so pleased for me. I always felt with her that she saw me as a person rather than a hospital number. I felt she wanted me to have that baby as much as I did and that she'd do all she could for me. It really made a difference to have someone that I felt listened to me. I don't think I could have carried on with any treatment if I hadn't felt that she understood what the miscarriage had meant to me.

Rosemary's fallopian tubes were badly damaged, partly due to the operation she had in her twenties. If there are adhesions or parts of the tube that are blocked it makes it very difficult for the egg to pass down into the uterus.

Microsurgery is a form of surgery using a microscope and very fine instruments. When this type of surgery is used on the fallopian tubes the surgeon tries to unblock the tubes as much as possible, clearing the way for the eggs to pass through.

After the microsurgery she said that she couldn't find one tube because it was hidden and bits were stuck together. Her description of my abdomen was, 'It's like a butcher's shop.' The prognosis wasn't very good but she had done some work on the remaining tube and she was hopeful – at least she'd given me the chance. In order to maximize my chances of conceiving she said that I should start taking the fertility drugs as soon as I'd healed really so that adhesions didn't start setting in. Although there was never a problem with my ovulation this would produce more eggs.

I took those for about six months and then in December of that year I had quite bad stomach pains and saw Mrs Varma. She suggested that I go in for a scan so that they could see what was happening and this was just before Christmas. I went and had a scan and she said to come back after Christmas for another one. I was to take things very easy.

The day of the scan it was confirmed I was pregnant. The girl that was doing the scan and Mrs Varma and David my husband were so happy and I didn't feel like that at all. It sounds really strange and it's probably hard for people to understand because it was something I'd wanted so much. But I think the first thing I felt was, 'I hope it doesn't end like the first one.'

Mrs Varma felt it was best that I stayed in hospital and had complete bed rest. I didn't even go home that day. She said that she felt because it was such a precious pregnancy after my having had the miscarriage I should just remain in hospital. The pains I had been getting were due to hyperstimulation of the ovaries and she wanted me to stay under observation because of that.

Complete bed-rest meant that I was in bed almost the whole day. I was allowed to get up in the morning and to go and have a shower or a bath and then I would spend the rest of the day in bed. I hadn't got any hobbies like knitting or sewing. I read a lot but it was hard to concentrate.

For me, being in bed all day, every day with people around me was a nightmare. I absolutely hated it. The staff were very kind. There were other women who were there for months and months. I think because they felt at the end of it they would have a baby they didn't seem to mind. I think from the beginning I just had a sixth sense that it wasn't going to work. I had no reason to believe that. My husband kept saying to me, 'You know you mustn't talk yourself into it, you must try and look on the bright side.' But in the same way that I'd resented him being able to walk away from the first miscarriage, I resented this. I thought, 'Well it's fine for you, you can just come and visit for an hour a day or whatever, and you can go home. You're still you, you're still free,' but I really felt as if I was a prisoner at times.

Looking back it must have been tough for him – he was trying to keep the home going all that time, he'd changed his job at work so he had all that pressure and he had to try and find time to come to see me at the end of a busy day, but I didn't see any of that, I just felt he was lucky.

Emotionally, I wasn't going to allow myself to get close to this baby. I think it was a safety valve. Because I'd put so much in to the first pregnancy, and it had meant so much to me, I was devastated when I lost it. It was a case of once bitten twice shy, that's not going to happen to me again. We didn't choose names or anything.

David was really hopeful and happy and thought everything would be fine. He was there when I had the scan and when they told us that I was pregnant. He was there from the beginning. I used to have scans each week and sometimes they would give me a photograph of the baby. To be honest I didn't understand it – they used to point to the screen and say, 'And here's the baby,' but I didn't really see anything at all.

I didn't want to allow myself to become attached in that way but David did; he kept the photographs and he was really interested to see them. It's funny to think that it's technology which allows a man to get slightly closer to the baby. I suppose for them it looks like proof. David likes technology and all the new inventions and for him it was absolutely wonderful that you could do this. I felt that it was because of the baby I was in this awful position of not being free and having all this noise around me and never being able to be on my own. If someone had said to me that at the end of the time I would definitely have a baby, I would have stayed in for the whole nine months. I would have felt absolutely fine but I just didn't feel fine about it and therefore I resented it.

Because of the superovulatory drugs I had developed a cyst on one of my ovaries. One of the reasons that I had the scans was so that they could measure the cyst and it did keep growing. I was dreading seven weeks because it was at six weeks that the last baby died so I was really frightened of getting to that time. I remember being in the scan room and being so terrified that they wouldn't hear a heart beat. There's always a part of you that's putting all your hopes into it. Mrs Varma was really happy and she said that the baby's heart was beating and everything was fine.

But gradually I began to feel really depressed. I thought, 'I can't stand this, I just need to have some space and a place where I can be quiet.' I wanted to go home and I asked if it would be possible. Mrs Varma said that if I really wanted to I could go home for weekends. In some ways it was worse when I came back on the Sunday because it was so peaceful at home.

Around week nine or ten I was at home most of the time, even though Mrs Varma had reservations about allowing this. I was given progesterone injections by the district nurse.

One morning I got up quite early, about six; I couldn't sleep and I went to the loo and I had exactly the same discharge as I'd had with the first miscarriage. Lots of people might have seen it and not panicked but it was exactly the same as I'd seen before and I thought, 'This is it, I'm going to lose this one, I knew it.' I called David and told him and he just virtually collapsed in a heap on the floor and started crying. I could see then that he had put so much into that baby. In fact it was almost as if our roles were reversed because he was so emotionally involved with this pregnancy in the same way I'd put a lot of my emotions into the first one.

He was just devastated and he was in no fit state to drive. I phoned a neighbour and asked her if she would take us to the hospital and she did. She took us to casualty and I explained to them that if they would just phone up to the ward I could just go straight up.

It was only about half past eight or nine o'clock when I eventually went up. I was settled and the doctor came with a mini scanning machine to the bedside. He said, 'Well there we are, Mrs Hall, everything is fine. The heart beat is there and there aren't any signs that anything is wrong so you take it easy and we'll see how things go'.

I don't know how long they'd been gone, maybe an hour, maybe longer, when I started bleeding. David was with me all the time. He called for the doctor. I was miscarrying. He asked David to go out and he said to me, 'I'm sorry but you're losing the baby.' David was really crying: he just put his hand against the wall and said, 'Why?'

I did have an awful lot of pain and they gave me injections. But it was so different from the first experience where no one knew me, no one knew what that baby meant, but here everyone knew what it meant to me and that really helped. One of the nurses held my hand and was so nice. I can remember saying, 'I'm really sorry about all the mess and everything.' She said, 'Don't worry, it doesn't matter,' and it was just so different that although it was still really upsetting and it was a really harrowing experience, I wasn't left with the emotional debris that I'd been left with the first time.

Helen had gone to the Bridge Fertility Clinic and the consultant had suggested that a new technique called GIFT (gamete intra-fallopian transfer) would be a suitable technique to try. They had been warned that it would be unlikely to work first time. The reason why she had GIFT rather than IVF was because Helen's fallopian tubes were normal and healthy. GIFT is when the doctors replace eggs and sperm in the women's fallopian tubes, which is a more natural environment for fertilization to take place than in the laboratory. The process is the same as the IVF which Miranda has described until the eggs have been retrieved.

The anaesthetist patted my hand and asked me to count to ten. I got to two and passed out. I was excited but I wasn't really nervous. I'd had the scan beforehand and been given the all clear that the eggs were mature and they could go ahead with the GIFT. I was about to have the transfer. They would retrieve the eggs from me, mix them with Jonathan's sperm in a tube outside my body and then put them back in the fallopian tubes. Instead of trying to create the best conditions for fertilization in the laboratory they put it all together in the natural environment. I was told that's why GIFT is generally thought to be more successful than IVF because it's closer to nature. So it's really just assisting the egg and sperm in part of the journey.

There had been a stage when it looked as if they would have to give up the attempt. It was about day twelve in my cycle and it seemed as if I had not produced any eggs. But I have a very long cycle and that part of the ovulation process doesn't happen until day sixteen or even eighteen. The consultant who had originally seen me, and knew about this, wasn't there but the other consultant eventually realized that it was going to take longer. I think in retrospect I was probably hyperstimulated because there were so many eggs. On the day that they retrieved them they took six healthy eggs and they put four back and kept two to fertilize in vitro. The two that were fertilized in the laboratory gave them an indication of what might be happening inside me. It's quite a positive thing if your eggs and sperm fertilize out of your body in the laboratory. It's not definite that the same will happen in utero but it probably should do.

GIFT (gamete intra-fallopian transfer) was initially used before standard IVF was developed, and was then abandoned. It was reintroduced in the early 1980s. The treatment is the same up to the point of egg retrieval. When the eggs have been collected they are examined and the healthiest will be chosen, mixed with the sperm and immediately placed in the fallopian tubes of the woman before fertilization. In IVF the fertilization would take place in laboratory conditions whereas in GIFT the egg and sperm are returned to the natural environment of the woman's tubal fluid.

High success rates have been claimed for GIFT but the figures are not as straightforward as they might seem. More recent trials show that it is not as successful as IVF. It is often suggested as a treatment for people who have unexplained infertility.

I don't actually know what happened to the two potential embryos. I assumed they just didn't continue to grow. I didn't question it too carefully. The thought did cross my mind but perhaps I didn't want to know the answer.

On the day of the egg retrieval we had come in very early, at about half past six because I remember it was half past seven in the morning that I was going in the lift. They took me down for a scan to make sure that the eggs were still there and they hadn't been released because if that happens then they can't do it – the eggs have gone and they can't retrieve them.

It was rather like Christmas morning and stocking opening – so much potential. Finally, after all the stages – and it's not an easy treatment, it is stressful and as I say, at one stage they didn't think I was going to be able to carry on – I felt quite a sense of achievement and so excited. Obviously my thought was maybe, maybe I'll get pregnant.

We went back to my room and the consultant who was doing the operation just popped in to say hello. He asked us whether we had all the information that we should have had. We said we thought so. He then went through how many eggs they might put back. The scan had shown three to four eggs and that was what I signed on the consent form. He said, 'You realize that there could be a chance of multiple birth, has this been discussed?' So we said, 'No, not really,' and he said, 'Well, there is but it's an outside chance and we're going to put back three to four eggs. Three to four eggs could mean that you would have three or four babies but that's not very likely.' We said, 'Oh fine.' So at that stage multiple birth was mentioned. I was aware of it.

Prior to this the discussions about the outcome were definitely focused on the idea that it probably wouldn't work and that I would need two or three attempts. I think their main aim was to get me used to the fact that the treatment is stressful and a pregnancy is not guaranteed.

The possibility of multiple birth was kept very low-key and I certainly didn't take it on board seriously. Now, when I think back, I just think how naive, why didn't I see it? How ludicrous to hear someone saying to you we're putting three or four eggs back, and not connect that immediately with three or four babies. I don't know why I didn't react more but I didn't understand the implications.

So the last thing I remembered was the anaesthetist. When I came round I had an incision near my tummy button and a smaller one down below it. One had two stitches in and the other had one stitch. During the operation they blew gas into my abdomen so afterwards I had awful pain in my rib cage. It is like a very weird feeling of wind.

I felt dreadful after this operation – very sick and dizzy. I also had an appalling headache and we actually stayed in until 6p.m. At this stage there isn't any way of knowing if things have gone well or badly, other than technically that everything had gone to plan. I think even through the haze of the anaesthetic I felt relief that it was over and then I was dreading the waiting.

Two weeks. It seemed endless. I didn't quite know what to do because I'd think, 'Oh no, it won't have worked, it won't have worked, why should it have worked, they've already warned me it probably won't work the first time.' I didn't feel pregnant. Not that I knew how I would feel but I thought I would feel sick or terribly tired. I felt fine. About two days after I'd had the GIFT done I had another really dreadful headache. I remember it was a very bright sunny day and I went to bed and I stayed in bed all day with the curtains shut. I couldn't bear any light. I've never known what that meant or whether it had any relevance.

Then I got a throat infection and my GP was going to give me some antibiotics for it. I mentioned that I'd had the GIFT done so the GP said, 'Well then you shouldn't really have any antibiotics, you'll just have to see this sore throat out because you could be pregnant.' My throat was so sore that I was really tempted to say, 'What do you mean, I'm not pregnant you know, just give me the antibiotics and get rid of my sore throat,' because I just didn't feel that I was.

I just didn't want to let myself build up an expectation. The last three days I did suddenly become incredibly tired ... I thought, 'Oh, I wonder' . . . and extraordinarily hungry. I was just so hungry and when Jonathan was at work I'd be tucking in to cheese and biscuits. Cooking supper at night, I would make myself puddings, which I never normally do – real nursery puddings, all stodgy ones.

I didn't consider myself to be remotely like a guinea pig at that stage. I feel it was probably naive of me but at the time I thought I was sort of on the threshold of everything changing. It was all very pioneering treatment and I was thinking how lucky I was that I had caught it at the right time. I felt rather privileged that all this technology was there and that they knew how to do it and that it would help us. I had complete faith in the doctors.

IVF

What are the success rates of IVF?

Because of the enormous interest which has continued since the birth of the first test-tube baby, many people have come to believe that IVF is the answer to the plight of the childless. In fact IVF has many disadvantages – as well as being very demanding both physically and emotionally, it is the most expensive and one of the least successful infertility treatments available.

As the experiences of the women in this book show, IVF is not even suitable for some of the people who go to the clinics for help. For those who do go on to be treated the chances of having a baby are still slim.

The Human Fertilization and Embryology Authority have published the most recently available results: in 1992 only 12.7 per cent of all IVF treatments produced a baby, only 13,791 women in Britain were treated by IVF and altogether 2,318 babies were born as a result of IVF in that year. However, many clinics are much more successful than these national average statistics might suggest.

What is the success rate of GIFT?

There are no national figures available for GIFT but some work has been done to compare its performance with that of IVF. A study carried out by the Hammersmith, comparing couples who were diagnosed with genuinely unexplained infertility, showed the following: after three cycles of GIFT at regular intervals over one year, 52 per cent of patients had a pregnancy; after three cycles of IVF over one year 84 per cent of comparable patients conceived successfully.

What other recent developments are there?

The most recent advances in reproductive technology have helped couples in which the male partner has very few sperm or sperm which do not fertilize. New techniques for assisting sperm that would otherwise be infertile include removing immature sperm directly from the man's testicle, drilling, tearing or chemically burning holes in the egg's outer coating, inserting sperm inside the zona (outer coating of the egg) or most recently using micro-injection to place the sperm into the body of the egg itself. This last technique is called ICSI – Intra-Cytoplasmic Sperm Injection. Researchers in Belgium developed the technique and more than three-hundred babies have been born around the world. It is too early to say that there are no dangers of congenital abnormalities developing in babies born through this technique, because there are too few cases to make up a proper research study.

How much does IVF cost?

There is much variation between the different centres. In some places the NHS will subsidize treatment by paying for the prescribed drugs. Probably the average amount being paid for a standard IVF assisted cycle is about £2,500. There are very few centres which are entirely funded by the National Health Service but some centres offer to help people in financial difficulties.

The Human Fertilization and Embryology Authority

One of the HFEA's intentions in the next year is to try to provide people with better information about the different centres. They feel that simply publishing success rates in terms of a take-home baby rate can be very misleading. Every patient is different and there are many factors which could contribute to a couple's infertility, so their requirements from a clinic will be different and the average success rates are not the best guide in choosing a clinic. They are hoping that now they have better data they will be able to give people better advice and more specific information. The address to write to is at the back of this book.

CHAPTER 6

PREGNANCY

The moment when a wanted pregnancy is confirmed is always exciting. When the build-up has been months, maybe years, of treatment and failed attempts, it is even more loaded with expectation. Often the excitement is shared by the entire staff of the IVF clinic.

Pregnancy is sometimes more complicated for a woman who has had trouble conceiving, as she may also find it difficult to carry a baby. Also, more assisted conceptions turn out to be multiple pregnancies. IVF and GIFT are less successful unless more than one embryo or egg is transferred at each attempt, but the more embryos that are transferred the greater the chance that twins or triplets will be conceived.

Miranda had collapsed under the grief she felt when the first IVF attempt failed. Although everyone told her that it was worth trying three times, and that she had a good chance of success, she also knew what it would cost her emotionally to go through it all again.

After the first IVF attempt failed I went through a long period of despair. It was always tinged with hope but it was a time of very complicated feelings. I almost had a deal with myself that I would keep saying, 'Oh it will never work, I'll never be a mother,' because then I could allow myself a few moments of hope. It was too painful to be in despair all the time and also too painful to allow myself to have hope.

I almost didn't go through with the next attempt. It was Clive who was keen that we should continue. I don't think I would have pulled out but in the early stages of sniffing the Buserelin I freaked out for a while. I was sure I couldn't face the ordeal. Clive said we should try and if it didn't work this time we would then consider whether we would ever do it again.

I carried on and as the process continued I started to get caught up in the excitement again. After the transfer I felt very peculiar, just as I had the last time, but I continued to feel peculiar even after the progesterone injections had stopped. I had cravings – salt, pepper, vinegar and spicy things. That went on until I had the pregnancy test.

That weekend we were moving house on the Monday and the pregnancy test was on the Friday. I took it easy with the packing and thought, 'Well if it is negative I will just have to delay any grieving until after this is done.' By the time the phone went, much as I was trying not to let myself, I was beginning to accept the possibility that I might be pregnant.

I bet they take it in turns because it must be so great to give people good news. They really enjoy it. She said, 'Hello Miranda, how are you feeling?' and I knew she wouldn't be asking me that unless . . . it just wasn't sombre . . . and then, 'You're pregnant.' This whoop of delight. And after all the negativity, the stress and anxiety, and grief and pain I can't believe I was so accepting. I just thought 'Yes, I'm pregnant.' I am so relieved that that was my reaction because I know lots of women just have nine months of anxiety, not being able to allow themselves to accept it.

I did have a scare – a bit of staining and discharge – but it was all right. I have taken it really easy since then. It is now twelve weeks.

Helen had four eggs placed back in her fallopian tubes with Jonathan's sperm. The eggs that had been taken out and mixed in the laboratory had fertilized, which they were told was a good sign. However, Helen did not feel pregnant and was preparing herself for disappointment. Two weeks after the transfer she went back to the clinic for a blood and urine test.

Jonathan answered the phone. It was Michael Chapman – my consultant. Jonathan started mouthing and gesturing to me on the phone – so I guessed who it was. I was feeling so low because I had convinced myself it hadn't worked and I was having even more stomach cramps and then he suddenly started smiling and making positive signs. I realized that he was saying, 'You're pregnant,' and I couldn't believe it. He put the phone down and we just didn't know what to say to each other and we kept looking at each other and laughing and thinking, 'Gosh, you know, I'm pregnant.' Then we thought we would tell someone so we rang up my father and he wasn't there and then we rang Jonathan's mother and she wasn't there either and nobody was there. So then we drove down to some friends who lived at the bottom of the road and they were there, so we did have someone to tell. We couldn't believe that it had happened and there was nobody to share it with.

Being pregnant was wonderful. I used to walk my dog Tiggy in the park and the maple trees were such wonderful colours. It was spring and I was pregnant and life was just wonderful, it was great. Finally we had become a normal couple. I wasn't prepared for how overwhelming that feeling would be and how much everything had affected me. When I was pregnant I thought, 'Well, I'm like all my girlfriends now; we can be the same as them, we're not going to be the ones without children.' That was great and I didn't realize that Jonathan had felt that so acutely as well, that it wasn't just me. I don't think we've ever been that happy.

Laura and Robert had gone through two assisted cycles but the eggs had never fertilized. Finally they decided to try another cycle using donor sperm.

I don't think I ever thought that it wouldn't work and I would be left childless. I think I just knew, and I just staked my heart on the belief that, come what may, however hard it seemed, I was going to be successful. Also, what I felt, and I hope it doesn't sound arrogant, was that, 'Thank goodness I'm OK, because if either of us were to have a problem, I'd far rather it was not me – because women carry children, and I would feel awful. Obviously it's a shared problem but I think that most couples would choose that it was the man who has the problem, because I think the whole issue of surrogacy is so tricky and so much more sensitive, whereas Donor Insemination is something that can be a hidden thing. So on the third attempt we just decided we would go for donor sperm.

I think at that point the doctor was a little unwise. Given that I had no physical problems – there were no blocked tubes, no evidence of endometriosis when they checked on the treatment, and that I was polycystic, and still quite young – they should have considered that a multiple birth was a serious risk. I think they were just thinking, 'Poor, poor people who've gone through this three times now, what can we do?'

They collected twenty eggs. To maximize the potential for pregnancy I had two lots of two eggs left in my tubes as part of the GIFT procedure. I went back two or three days later, and I had a further two eggs or embryos implanted with embryo transplant. The ones used for the transplant were fresh; the rest were then frozen. So I think really, that was unwise, and I'm sure people looking at it now would say let's take a step back – we are starting with another clean piece of paper here.

With hindsight I would have preferred to forget the assisted drug cycle and have started by trying ordinary insemination which is a very simple, inexpensive procedure. I wouldn't have had to go through the egg retrieval, and all those things which are not only expensive, but also involve a general anaesthetic. A lot of people who have donor insemination don't go through any treatment really.

Unfortunately I never thought about it until much later, until it was far too late. So a few days after the embryos were put in I had the most appalling reaction. Because I was pregnant, I had the reaction many women with polycystic ovaries describe. What happens is that every egg follicle becomes like a factory of progesterone. Most women have the amount that is produced by one follicle, or maybe if they have twins there is twice as much. But I had something like twenty follicles pumping out progesterone, and the hormones released when you are newly pregnant, and I had the most dreadful symptoms: I remember one morning getting up and having a shower – it was about five or six days after I'd had the embryos put in – and I felt absolutely awful, and had to sit down, I thought I was going to faint. I got Robert and crawled into bed. My heart was going, and I didn't feel right in myself in any way. My genitals had swollen up, the labia were the size of salamis.

I started to panic. I rang the hospital and was told that this is what happens in polycystic cases when there's a pregnancy. So, for about three days I felt really ghastly.

Hyperstimulation syndrome occasionally happens when women have been treated with HMG – human menopausal gonadotrophin (Pergonal or Humegon). It is a mixture of the pituitary hormones LH and FSH which stimulate the ovaries. It's given in the early part of the cycle and can lead to the ovary producing many follicles and eggs. The effect can be very powerful and has to be monitored carefully. For Laura and women like her, it can result in hyper-stimulation of the ovaries. Most of the hyperstimulation simply causes mild abdominal pain for a few days. On occasion, bed rest is needed. The ovaries become very large and cystic. The pregnancy exacerbates the problems in about 1-2 per cent of women, when it can turn into a serious condition which requires the woman to be in hospital. (Early in 1994 a woman called Joanne Harris died of this condition.)

I still didn't know for sure that I was pregnant. I had to go to the hospital for the test. I was so ill that I didn't want to believe it until it was confirmed. They took the test and the consultant said, 'You are pregnant'. So I phoned Robert up straight away and he said in a hesitant way, 'What? Are you phoning us with good news?' and he started to cry. He had been so worried it wasn't going to work. I passed the phone to the consultant and he said, 'You're going to be a Daddy, Robert.' All I could hear was the sobbing and I said, 'Come home, come home.' It was wonderful – so exciting. When we got home we wept. Robert was so relieved because he said he had worried that it would just never happen. After that he got really involved and came to all the appointments.

Both Laura and Helen knew there was a possibility they were pregnant with more than one baby. After a pregnancy is confirmed the usual procedure is to arrange an ultrasound scan for the sixth or seventh week. The reason for the timing is that there is an increased risk with assisted conceptions of ectopic pregnancy. This is when the cells which become the placenta embed in the fallopian tube rather than the uterus, and the embryo starts to develop there. If this happens the growing embryo may burst the tube, which is very dangerous for the mother and means that the baby cannot survive.

Helen and Jonathan were completely delighted to know that the treatment had been successful and she was pregnant. Their joy was only slightly spoilt by the knowledge that Jonathan's job was going to require that he work in Liverpool full time.

The scan room was very dark, no lights on and blacked-out windows, and you could hear the hum of the scanning machine. My clothes were pulled up and a sort of cold jelly stuff was squirted on to my stomach. They have a probe which they move up and down on you and they dig that in quite hard; it doesn't really hurt, it's just slightly uncomfortable. Then the man said, 'Oh yes, here's a baby,' and then there was a silence.

I remember he moved the probe around more and then asked for someone to be called in. The embryologist came and said, 'Oh no, Michael's not here.' (Michael Chapman was my consultant.) I was told then that they had seen there was more than one embryo. He then started to show me and said, 'Well here's two and there's a third one,' and they didn't actually tell me that there was a shadow of the fourth. Sometimes embryos can be reabsorbed and because it was so shadowy and the heart wasn't as strong, it wasn't actually mentioned. I remember everybody talking and all the excitement and somebody did ask how I felt, and I said, 'Oh, all right,' but I knew they weren't really asking to know.

Everybody was standing above me talking about it. I felt invisible. It wasn't that I wanted to be the centre of attention but I felt very left out. It was my body they were scanning and discussing. I remember there was a bathroom just next door so I went in and was wiping the jelly off and wiping my hands. I was absolutely petrified and I thought what on earth does this mean? I was completely in awe and was thinking what have I done?

In the other room Jonathan was joking in a very happy-go-lucky optimistic way, 'Oh well, great – we'll only have to do it once' – which is what everybody says. Then there was the medical conversation going on above my head. Eventually one of the embryologists did say to me, 'You don't have any babies until they are born and they are at home in their cots; that's when you can say, "I've got two babies or three babies." There's a long way to go, and a lot can happen,' and then he said, 'But don't be negative about it either, don't lose heart but we're going to have to see you again quite soon – this isn't what we expected.'

Eventually I started to think – this has happened and I can't change any of it. I had to deal with it from now even though it wasn't what I was prepared for. Then rather silly thoughts were coming to my head – 'How am I going to buy four cots and how am I going to fit four cots in a room' – and then, 'Gosh, what a lot of nappies I'm going to have to buy.' With hindsight that seems ridiculous.

By this time I knew that Jonathan was going to be working in the north of England for at least the next two years. How was I going to look after four babies? With the best will in the world, wherever he was working he would be at work every day, so it was obviously going to fall to me. I didn't see how we were going to afford to have a nanny. We'd always said that if I managed to get pregnant, thinking it would be one baby then, we would try and pay for some help directly after the baby was born. I had considered joining him in Liverpool but given the treatment and now the fact that it was not going to be a straightforward pregnancy I would have to be in London.

Gradually I began to look forward to it all. I couldn't imagine what I might look like with four babies inside. I have always been thin. I eat like a horse and my friends are furious because I can eat cream cakes and things that they'd love to eat and it doesn't seem to have any effect on me. But I'm not a frail flower. It never entered my head that I wouldn't cope.

I had an appointment booked to see Michael Chapman at Easter time. I was really excited, it was the day before Good Friday. I was waiting at the hospital at about 2p.m. and I knew that Jonathan had already left Lancashire and was coming down. We would have a few days together. I'd been told that Michael Chapman wanted to see me and talk to me. I'd come very positively, thinking, 'Oh, he's going to talk to me about the pregnancy.' Well, obviously he was but not in the way that I envisaged.

Before this I didn't have any counselling but Michael Chapman talked to me about carrying quads. He had said that it wasn't ideal and he gave me all the medical details. He tried to suggest not looking too far ahead – one step at a time – so he would only really allow me to think two weeks ahead.

He said he wanted to discuss selective termination – reducing the number of foetuses. It would be reduced by two. The papers he gave me to read about it were all American. He said that he wouldn't carry out the procedure himself but that there were hospitals where I could have it done. They use an ultrasound scanner and they inject the heart of the foetus with potassium. I remember asking whether I would be conscious for this and he said that I would. I did get really upset and remember saying to him, 'Well, they might just be foetuses to you but to me they're babies. I am pregnant, I am having babies, they're mine, they're Jonathan's.'

I felt very strongly that, to a degree, I'd already interfered with nature. I'd had the treatment done and this was the result and I should go forward with the pregnancy. I remember leaping up out of my chair and going out of the room and saying that I didn't want selective reduction – it sounded an awful procedure. I know he didn't do it to upset me. I was just totally unprepared for the conversation I had with him. I had thought it was going to be a positive one – I had thought he would say that I might need more care than during a normal pregnancy. But I hadn't expected that.

I came home and I remember walking around in the garden and clutching my stomach, thinking, 'Well I don't want to lose them.' I can't say I don't agree with abortion under any circumstances but I'm not particularly pro-abortion. I don't know what I would have done if Jonathan had felt differently but he didn't; I was fairly sure that he wouldn't but I didn't tell him what to think.

When I went back to Michael Chapman he was very supportive. He said he wouldn't say which course I should take. It was an option that he had to tell me about because it was there. It had to be my choice and I completely respect him for that and I always will do.

At that time I had a few ideas about the risks of multiple pregnancy – I'd been warned they would probably be early. But in my mind I had the idea this meant three weeks early, which wouldn't have mattered much. I also knew that I'd spend a little bit of extra time in hospital with them afterwards but I imagined this would be two weeks instead of five days. I'd also been told I'd have a caesarian but I was actually quite relieved. I thought, 'Yes, too right with four.' So that wasn't a surprise. But my mind was clearly focused on four babies at the end of eight or nine months.

L aura had been convinced she would get pregnant eventually and now she was. She and Robert started to make plans and realized the financial implications of children. They were both self-employed and Robert's business was not particularly secure at that time.

Six weeks later I went to have a scan to check that all was well, and found out that I was carrying triplets. We were so pleased. Everyone had said that it might be twins but to have triplets was just so amazing. I felt like I was a million dollars and Super-mum. In one go I was going to catch up with all my friends and family. It had all been well worth it.

But then we started to think about three babies. There was panic around my husband's business, which he'd been setting up in Birmingham. In the end it was a financial disaster, with a capital D. But we were living in a two-bedroomed cottage, so we had to move to a bigger house because there was no way we could fit three cots in, or three cribs or anything. So we bought a bigger house, which had room for a nanny and guests and a nursery with three lots of baby things. We were financially really strapped; we couldn't afford to get it done up.

My parents were over. We're from South Africa – but they now live six months of the year in Spain, and six months in South Africa. They gave us a lot of grief. They would go on about us being about to have a family, and Robert not providing, and this is dreadful and that's dreadful, so we felt enormous stress from them. They would do things like sort of help by stripping wallpaper, but complain so much that I'd rather have stripped the wallpaper myself.

The pregnancy began and this all happened in January 1989. My due date was around the end of September. By the end of June or beginning of July my parents were still staying and I was under a lot of stress with them. I'd been absolutely miserable having them in the house, but I didn't have the strength to say, 'Go', because basically they were just making me feel totally inadequate about everything. At that time they had really set themselves up in conflict with Robert. They had a list of complaints: we were about to have triplets, Robert was setting up a business and was away a lot, and the house was basically a building-site. They just thought it too appalling for words and there was a lot of moaning that I could have done without.

As far as I was concerned I had a bed, the bedroom was sort of comfortable, the kitchen was comfortable, and I would have just happily lain and got big. But because of the pressure from my parents I felt I had to get on and get the house sorted out. So I was madly busy decorating and painting when I should have been resting. Robert was working until two or three in the morning getting all his computer work done and my mother would imply that he was out with the lads.

Helen was expecting four babies in London and Jonathan was working full-time near Liverpool. They were also struggling with the idea of how they were going to cope with the financial implications of a multiple birth.

Jonathan left London for Lancashire just after the pregnancy result. He went to run the Northern side of the business he worked in – it provided luxury food for restaurants and his job was to run a quail farm and organize the game collection from the grouse moors. It was a bit of a blow for me. By then I knew that it was a multiple birth and that he wasn't going to be there during the week, every week. I went in to hospital to have bed-rest rather earlier perhaps than I would have done if Jonathan had been at home.

Our house was in a terrible state because we'd only recently bought it. It needed a new roof, it needed to be rewired, replumbed, have central heating put in – really everything you can possibly think of. The plaster in the house was so bad that it was bulging off the walls and when one went to switch on a light the light socket was sticking out of the wall and bits of plaster would fall off as you turned the lights on or off. All the floorboards needed replacing, and a damp course had to be put in. So it was like living in a building site.

But when you're pregnant you have this eternal optimism. I think hormones take over and I found that I was in a very benign state. I would just switch off and turn a blind eye and a blind ear to it and think, 'Oh well, by the time I come home with these babies this will all be done.' I didn't really question quite how that was going to happen but I knew it was something that I physically couldn't do anything about – there was no way I could get up a ladder and start painting and plastering.

At sixteen weeks I had something called a suture put in. Apparently it is rather like a drawstring on a purse – it tightens up the neck of the womb. It was felt there would be quite a lot of pressure and strain on the cervix. Unfortunately things didn't go quite as planned and it set off a chain of events that made my uterus become very irritable and I had to stay in hospital for a lot longer than planned. Normally one is only in overnight but when I woke up I was on a salbutamol drip, which was to stop any contractions. I hadn't been warned about this. They had to put the rate of the salbutamol up and up which then made my heart-rate go up a lot and it also made me very sick. Apparently before they developed the use of salbutamol, they used to give women in this condition alcohol.

Salbutamol is a drug which is given to relax the uterine contractions. It is given through a drip because the level of the drug in the blood-stream can then be kept at a constant level. It can also be given orally.

By twenty-one weeks I was feeling very tired and becoming larger all the time. I also found it very difficult to breathe because my diaphragm was being pushed up. I had appalling indigestion.

Eventually my uterus became more irritable and I needed to stay in hospital during the week. When my blood pressure started to go up I then had to go in to the London Bridge Hospital permanently and stay on bed rest. I found it quite difficult to cope with because it had happened so suddenly. I felt very powerless because all the decisions had been taken away from me.

I loathe feeling out of control. I'm not very good at relaxing and having a drink and getting squiffy, because I can't bear to be out of control. I'm an organized, efficient sort of person and I like to plan things. I'm an obsessive list-maker and if I had known I was going in to hospital I would have made copious lists and I hadn't got a list at all; everything was left behind and lots of things I needed weren't there.

I was so overwhelmed by the fact that I felt so impotent. Certainly, during the last four weeks of the pregnancy I seemed to be just a big lump pinned to a bed and I couldn't move. I knew I shouldn't try and move because it was putting the babies at risk and the blood pressure was going up and up and up, but I'm not the sort of person to stand back and not try and participate.

I did find it very difficult and once the babies were born I was quite unprepared for the force, the strength of my feelings for them and how overwhelming love is. Health professionals shouldn't underestimate that strength and the value of it and what it can do, because a mother's love for her babies is untouchable and probably the most powerful love that there is. Nothing diminishes it.

Throughout her pregnancy with three babies Laura had been trying to make the new house habitable. She also had her parents staying with her. It was now twenty-six weeks into the pregnancy.

I woke up very early one morning feeling really uncomfortable. I was in labour although it took me a while to realize it. I phoned Robert at the office, and said can you come home, and he came home and said, 'What's the matter?', and I said, 'I think I've eaten something which doesn't agree with me, I feel awful.' I kept having diarrhoea, and didn't realize that that's what a lot of women have when they go into labour – everything starts working at once. It took me about, I suppose, five contractions, which would have been over about two hours, to pick up there was some rhythm to it, and that it wasn't like a normal tummy cramp, my whole uterus was going. I said to Robert, 'Oh God, I think I've gone into labour.'

But even then I didn't believe it. I was still only twenty-six weeks pregnant, though I was very big. I'd been told that everything was going really well, but looking back on it I had a crap doctor at the hospital. I went to him saying I was concerned at how big I was getting and how quickly, and he said it was to be expected as I was having triplets. He was a consultant, not a junior doctor. I actually had excess fluid around each baby, which meant that I really was increasing in size very quickly.

I'd thought while I was enlarging, 'Aren't I doing well.' But I started to get worried because I was in fact becoming inches bigger by the day. I thought, 'Well obviously this must be going right,' – the doctor had even made me feel rather like a silly little girl. But I was getting visibly bigger in front of my eyes.

I was supposed to be seeing the doctor on the Monday, and I went into labour on the Sunday night. At the hospital I was in labour for five days, with a drip. It would stop, and then a few hours later it would start again, and they'd up my dose, and it was all pretty unpleasant. It was a drug like salbutamol, a drug they give asthmatics, and there's only so much they can give you because it plays havoc with your heart. I felt I was in overdrive, with my heart pumping enormously, so it seems strange that for some reason the drug calms your uterus down. I don't know quite how it works, but it's a bit like being on Ventolin, you're on a bit of a rush.

Finally I realized that I was having contractions every three minutes and by that point there was nothing that could be done. I was trying to deny that I was in labour. My mother, Robert and my girlfriend Sarah, who is a nurse, would take turns sitting in with me. Sarah realized what was going on and went to get a doctor who came in and examined me. I was 5cm dilated and it became an emergency caesarean mainly to get the children out quickly to give them the best chance.

I still had a wilful naiveté that they were going to be OK. Twenty-six weeks seemed quite a long way advanced; I'd heard of children born at twenty-three or twenty-four weeks who had survived. I was told that, if you've been in labour for some time the children get some amount of adrenalin, which is good for them, it puts them on a better standing. Girls have a greater survival rate so when we knew we had three girls I thought, 'Well, they're going to be fine'.

Generally, not just in multiple births, girl babies are thought to have a better chance of survival than boys. More boy babies are born overall.

The reason my parents were over was because my father was going over to South America on a trip. He'd gone when I'd been in labour, thinking things would be fine and that they'd stopped the labour, and assuming I'd spend the rest of my pregnancy in hospital. Little could any of us have known that only days later I'd be actually giving birth.

When the girls were born I think there were twenty-something people in the delivery suite. There was actually a really nice atmosphere. It was exciting; I refused to think that anything was going to go wrong with the birth at all. I kept thinking it was going better than expected. I was told that they wouldn't make a noise, and Isobel sort of mewed like a kitten. I was told that they'd weigh one and a half pounds if they were lucky, and Isobel was 1lb 15oz, Caitlin was 2lb 2oz, and Megan, the tiniest, was 1lb 10oz. So although they seemed incredibly tiny they were all bigger than I had expected. So to me, everything seemed to point to the fact that they were going to be OK. It was going to be hard but they were going to be OK.

I hadn't really read anything about the negative side of premature births. Unconsciously I must have worried a bit because something had made me take out a couple of books on premature births to get to grips with what incubators are like, and what happens, the care they would need, or whatever. But, more from an optimistic point of view, thinking, 'It's unlikely I'm going to go through to forty weeks with these children.'

After their birth they took photographs of them, and I was put on a ward with women who all had their children with them, but I didn't feel bad about it at that point. I thought, 'Oh well, they've all got their children but mine are up in special care; I'm special, as I've had three baby girls, and isn't it wonderfully exciting.'

Because it had been non-stop, Robert went home and crashed to sleep in bed. The next morning he didn't hear the phone ringing and ringing and ringing. It was me trying to get him to come, because my mother needed to go. He finally got a lift about nine, and then my mother went off to lunch with a friend, thinking of herself as the proud grandmother and 'my daughter's just had triplets'. We were all still pretty excited.

Helen's consultant had started to worry about her blood pressure and was keeping her in the hospital to monitor the pregnancy. She had now reached the twenty-eighth week of gestation with four babies.

It was on a Friday that my blood pressure went higher and higher. I was just lying in my hospital bed with nobody requiring me to move at all. I had come to love the view of the river. Increasingly I found I couldn't concentrate on people talking to me for very long and I'd more or less fall asleep. I didn't seem to be able to comprehend what they were saying to me. On the Saturday Jonathan was down from Lancashire and he was going to a friend's stag night that evening and I remember being aware of that and not happy about it.

It was a very sunny day and Jonathan was watching tennis on the television. I was feeling so peculiar. I was looking out and all these lights went across my eyes, little white wiggly lines and there was an extraordinary ringing, buzzing sound in my ears and that was all I could hear. Everything else, all normal sound went. A nurse came in a little while later and I said, 'Oh I'm having lights go across my eyes,' and she said, 'Oh it's probably the sun.' I was very drowsy and I had a headache. Jonathan went off and said goodbye and there was something in me that was concerned that he was going. I said, 'Well you will ring when you get there won't you and leave a number.'

Between six and seven that evening my consultant Michael Chapman came in. I remember asking him if pregnancy ever affects your eyes. He looked at me very closely and I said, 'I've had these white wiggly lines going across my eyes,' and he said, 'Oh,' – very calmly. I found out afterwards he sauntered out of the room and got outside and said, 'Right, give me the phone; I'm going to phone Guy's (Hospital). I want you to monitor her very closely and I want fluid levels done.' Then he came back in not conveying any panic at all.

All through the pregnancy I'd had this book called *Pregnancy* by Gordon Bourne. It was my security blanket and I had read and read and read it so that it was all thumb-marked. I was always peering in to this book when Michael came in. He used to dread me saying, 'I've been reading my book and it says such and such.' He'd sort of brace himself and think, 'Oh, what's she going to ask now.' But this time he actually asked me where my book was. I said, 'I can't read now so it's across there,' and pointed to the shelf. He turned to a section and said, 'What has happened to you now is you've gone beyond having pre-eclampsia, you are toxic. It's called toxaemia and this is what it means – there is no question now that you can stay here; you'll be transferred to Guy's tomorrow, first thing at nine in the morning.'

Pre-eclamptic toxaemia is usually just referred to as pre-eclampsia. It rarely occurs before the twentieth week of pregnancy and its cause is unknown. It usually develops gradually and if a woman shows any of the symptoms she will be very carefully monitored. If it continues without intervention, the blood pressure continues to rise, headaches develop, some women, like Helen, experience visual disturbance, mental dullness and, on very rare occasions, fits in the later stages.

It is a very dangerous condition, both for the mother and the baby. The risks to the unborn baby will increase as the blood pressure rises. There is always a possibility of premature labour because the placenta may start not to function properly.

Once pre-eclampsia has developed the treatment is admission to hospital, bed-rest, sedation, and monitoring of the kidney function and blood pressure. If the mother becomes fully eclamptic, it is likely that an emergency caesarian section would be carried out: the mother's life is the priority.

I know it sounds ridiculous but the first thing I said was, 'Oh, I've got to pack all my things.' Then I tried to concentrate and asked what it meant and would it hurt the babies and he said, 'Well it is very serious – you are ill and if you deteriorate at all from now on you will be transferred earlier.'

I think it was about eight in the evening then. One of the nurses I knew very well came in and I remember saying, 'Please will you ring Jonathan, will you tell him what's going on.' She told me, 'We've already rung him but he's had some armagnac, so he's not going to drive back this evening, but he knows and he will be back early in the morning.'

I was very nervous about going to Guy's because I had visited it and it's a very different type of hospital. Michael was very insistent that I had to be there because they had midwives there and I would be on the labour ward and that the care that I would receive there would be much better and far more appropriate than at the London Bridge hospital. It isn't licensed for birth and so I could never have stayed anyway.

That evening I drifted in and out of consciousness. The nurses would

113

take my temperature and blood pressure. At one point I woke up with a start and went in to really very strong contractions. The next thing I knew they were saying, 'We've rung Michael and he's on his way and you're not going to be staying here tonight.'

My main concern was for the babies. I remember lying with my hand on this great big bump and I could feel them so I thought that they must be all right. I don't think I was aware of the danger to myself – I couldn't read the book because I couldn't concentrate.

Because I didn't realize how ill I was, I didn't know that having toxaemia meant I couldn't carry on being pregnant. I just thought this was yet another hiccup and I'd be on salbutamol and more strict bed-rest. It wasn't that no one told me – I don't think I was in a fit state to receive any information. In fact the move to the other hospital was so that I could give birth but I didn't realize how imminent it was.

Michael came back and we went to Guy's. I was put into a room – I found that I couldn't lie on a bed because it was just too uncomfortable so I had to try to sleep on a bean bag. In the private hospital I had been given a special spenco mattress for my bed – there was nothing like that here.

I couldn't lie down flat because I couldn't breathe at all. It was partly that Freddy, who was lying across the top of the others, had pushed up my diaphragm so high. But also my lungs had a lot of fluid on them which is why I'd been coughing so much. My lungs weren't inflating properly so I found it very difficult.

Michael Chapman stayed the night but he decided he wasn't going to sleep in the room with me so he had a room just round the corner and told the nurse that if there was any change at all he was to be woken up straight away. I had a nurse who was in the room with me most of the rest of that night and morning.

Then I did start to panic because everything had changed and the room was so stark and alien and I didn't know any of the nurses and it was all so different. I wished that Jonathan was in the hospital and not down in Kent or wherever his stag night had been. I felt very alone and I was so out of control by then there was nothing I could do and I felt events were completely overtaking me.

In the early morning they decided that they were going to have to catheterize me which was awful, I absolutely hated it. I remember arguing and arguing with the registrar that I didn't want to have it done and it wasn't necessary and that no, I was not going to lie in bed and be catheterized and as long as I could stand I would get up to the loo. She was saying, 'No, you won't at all, you are not getting out of bed not even to do that, that's why you're being catheterized.' I said, 'I'm sure that Michael hasn't said that this must be done,' and she said, 'Yes, he has.' I just found it terribly humiliating and embarrassing. I wasn't allowed out of bed.

I had a monitor on that was listening to the babies' heart-rates. It was difficult to hear because there were four of them and there was so much movement from them. I had at least two drips up, one was salbutamol and I had a dextrose saline drip up because I couldn't eat. Then they started to scan me. In the meantime Jonathan had come back. I remember asking him when he had to go back and he said the consultant had told him he shouldn't because I would probably give birth some time that week. I was remonstrating that I couldn't and then I don't really remember any more. I would understand things for about a minute but I couldn't retain them, I didn't carry on understanding them.

After the scans I was worried because I knew that Freddy was in distress. His heart-rate was so weak. He was much smaller than the others and I remember just being so worried about him. All I wanted was for him to be all right. I didn't know if he was a boy or a girl, all I knew was that one of the babies was ill and was in distress and that was what I found so unbearable. I was terrified of losing them and what was going to happen. At this stage the others were moving around and they seemed to have good heart-rates.

What I didn't know was that there was another panic going on behind the scenes. Overnight there had been several premature babies born and all the cot spaces at Guy's had gone. I couldn't have the babies there. While I was lying in bed there was a frantic panic of ringing other hospitals and trying to arrange a transfer. Michael Chapman told me that another consultant, Professor Grodzinskas, who had in fact performed my GIFT, was going to take over, with a paediatrician he worked with at the Royal London, Dr Graeme Snodgrass. There were at least three cot spaces there, maybe four, and that was where I was going to be transferred because the babies had to be born and quite soon. The Royal London was in Whitechapel; Michael was going to accompany me.

My main memory of the ambulance journey is my leg falling off the stretcher thing. I was so fat and heavy because of the toxaemia and I couldn't get it back on again and I had to lie there and wait for Michael to pick my leg up. This hideous, swollen fat leg – I couldn't believe it was a part of me. It was an incredibly hot day, and I didn't know where we were going. They were debating whether to use the siren as well as the blue light, and I remember saying, 'Please don't. No, please no,' because my head hurt so much, and I couldn't bear noise – I just didn't want to hear it. Sirens are panicky things, they mean there's something very wrong, and although I knew there was a lot wrong I didn't want that reinforced.

They took me straight up to the Labour Ward. There was a very officious nurse who was arguing with Michael Chapman as to whether I should be there. What was wrong with me anyway? I remember lying and thinking – this is such a ridiculous conversation. Michael was so frustrated with her, and he said, 'Well, she's on the Labour Ward because she is in premature labour, she's threatening to give birth now, that's why she's on salbutamol, that's why she's on these drips.' The nurse went away, then very grudgingly came back with a proper drip stand. So that was my first impression of the Royal London. It was yet another hospital, and it was a very alien hospital and not at all friendly.

I didn't go to theatre until Tuesday. Jonathan was allowed to stay with me. In the next room there was another mother in labour. It was just awful because she was shrieking a lot, and she was saying really awful things about not wanting the baby. And I was lying there thinking, 'Well, I'd like to be giving birth and I'd like it to be all right, and I wish that one of my babies wasn't very ill.'

Great chunks of my memory are missing because I was in and out of sleep. I remember being shaved and seeing Jonathan with one of those strange hats on. I also remember looking up from the trolly at pipes – endless plumbing pipes bound in foil and wire. Somehow they remind me of the suffocating feeling.

When I got down to the theatres, Michael came to talk to me, and said that he was there and I wasn't to worry. Jonathan told me afterwards that they had told him that if I didn't pick up properly after the operation and had any difficulties in breathing I would go into Intensive Care, but I had no idea of that at all.

There were so many people around. I think there were about twenty-eight or twenty-nine people in the theatre. I was introduced to the anaesthetist, who told me to lie down. I remember panicking and saying to him, 'I can't lie down because if I lie down I can't breathe, I can't bear to lie down, I don't want to lie down, please don't make me lie down.' And he said, 'It'll be all right because when you lie down I'll put this mask over you and that will help you to breathe. You will be able to breathe.' And they got my shoulders, and he was pushing me down and I was fighting because I didn't want to lie down because I knew I couldn't breathe. And then the mask came, and I don't remember anything else.

Multiple Birth

Is there a higher risk of a multiple birth with infertility treatment?

All treatments which use drugs to stimulate the ovaries to produce several eggs increase the risk of more than one baby being conceived.

Before the introduction of infertility treatment the triplet rate in the UK used to be about 1 in every 10,000 maternities. This figure has trebled since the early Eighties and in 1992 the rate was 1 in 3,400, with 225 sets of triplets, 8 sets of quadruplets, and 1 set of quintuplets born after twenty-four weeks' gestation.

Today about one third of higher order births occur naturally, one third following IVF and GIFT treatments and one third from ovulation-inducing drugs alone. The 1993 report of the Human Fertilization and Embryology Authority showed that in the UK 29.1 per cent of IVF pregnancies were multiple – 24.5 per cent were twins and 4.6 per cent were triplets.

Is there a restriction about how many eggs can be put back?

In 1991 the Human Fertilization and Embryology Authority was established by the HFE Act of Parliament. Centres offering treatment have to be licensed and in order to be licensed they must abide by the Code of Practice. This stipulates that no more than three embryos may be transferred in assisted conception procedures. However there are no restrictions in the use of ovulation-inducing drugs and the Multiple Birth Association feels that more judicious use and careful monitoring is needed.

Why are multiple births to be avoided?

The first reason is that they increase the risk of a premature delivery. An average delivery for a single baby is at forty weeks. The average length for twins is thirty-seven weeks, triplets thirty-four weeks and quads thirty-three weeks. Another reason is that although for someone who has been unable to conceive the idea of three or four babies at once seems ideal, the reality of looking after them in the early stages is extremely difficult. Multiple births, particularly those of more than two infants, bring with them financial, physical and emotional stress to many of their families. Postnatal depression is more common in mothers of twins. Children of multiple births are also more likely to suffer from language delay and have an increased risk of later reading problems.

What effect does premature birth have on the babies?

Babies that are born from multiple pregnancies tend to be smaller, partly because they are born earlier and partly because they grow less well in the later part of the pregnancy. A woman's womb is able to nourish up to four babies very well until the twenty-sixth week of pregnancy. This is a critical time because if the babies are born at this stage and are well nourished they have a good chance of healthy survival.

After twenty-six weeks of pregnancy the growth rate of multiples is progressively slower than singletons, depending on how many babies are present. A twin is 4.6 times more likely to die around the time of the birth than a single baby, for triplets the same figure is 12 times and for quads it is 16 times.

Are they more likely to be disabled?

The incidence of disability is higher in multiple births but there are no exact figures available for the UK. In Western Australia the number of babies born with cerebral palsy per thousand births was 2.4 for singletons, 6.3 for twins and 32 for triplets.

> *The two women, Laura and Helen, whose experiences are included here are not intended to be representative of the vast majority of multiple births. There is also no implication that what happened to them was an inevitable consequence of the reproductive medical techniques which they underwent. Many people will find the next chapter upsetting, but it does represent a fundamental aspect of the experience of infertility.*

CHAPTER 7

PREMATURE BIRTH

Multiple pregnancy carries with it a risk of premature birth. A pregnancy is said to be at term by thirty-seven weeks, and for single babies the average time of gestation is forty weeks. The average week of pregnancy for triplets to be born is thirty-four and for quads thirty-three. Although there are some medical procedures which can delay the birth, it is not always possible to prevent it. Sometimes the babies stand a better chance of survival if the birth goes ahead. With a multiple pregnancy of three or four babies, it is known that the capacity of the woman's body's to carry and nourish the babies after the twenty-sixth week diminishes.

Laura's and Helen's experiences illustrate some of the risks of multiple pregnancy and birth, but they are by no means representative of the vast majority of such births which take place.

Laura had gone into labour at twenty-six weeks. The medical staff had tried to control the contractions with a drug called salbutamol, but by the evening of the fifth day Laura was feeling contractions every three minutes and the birth was imminent. In the delivery room there were twenty people waiting to rush the three little girls off to the neonatal ward.

Laura was confident they would survive. She comforted herself with the thought that babies of twenty-four weeks' gestation had lived and she had been told that girls had a better chance. The morning after the birth she and Robert were waiting on the maternity ward to go and see the babies in their incubators.

At 11 o'clock they told me that Megan was not going to make it. I'd had them at about three in the morning. It came as a complete shock. I was just so sure they'd make it.

Premature babies often have problems with their lungs. I was told that twenty-eight weeks is the magical time when the lungs are developed. The children's lungs were not developed, and they needed oxygen to keep them alive, but the oxygen sometimes actually causes damage. Their little lungs were like the finest type of tissue paper. When they're having oxygen put inside their system, because they are no longer getting oxygen through their mother, it just perforates the lungs. Lung disease is the major cause of death with that age of child.

So we went up to the ward to see Megan. As I'd had a caesarean, I felt weird. The whole thing was almost surreal at that point. I had thought that it was going to be so special to have these triplets. When I got up there she was even tinier than I remembered; she just seemed so small. And they lifted her out of the incubator and put her on my knee, and she was still attached to all these tubes and everything, and it just seemed inhumane; I thought at the time, 'If there's anything they could do to make her live, then let them do it, but if there isn't, just take all this away – it's just so mechanical.' And they said there was nothing they could do, but they'd kept her attached to them for me to get up there, I suppose.

They were absolutely fabulous in the special care baby unit; I'm sure it's the same the country over, but I think they were just superb. They took us into a little side room and wrapped Megan up and we held her, thinking well, we had triplets, we had three, but now we've got twins. But I thought, everyone will see us out walking and say, 'Oh, how lovely, you've got twins,' and I was already trying to work out how I would say, 'No, I've had triplets', because at that point, I thought I'd be denying Megan if everyone thought that all we'd had was twins.

It was intensely emotional. Afterwards I felt completely and utterly numbed. I'd had five days with very little sleep at all, and then a caesarean and I felt completely out of it.

We went back down to the ward, and at that point it really hurt to be on a ward with women who were breastfeeding six pound, seven pound, eight pound babies. There was a deadly hush when we arrived, and I knew that everybody knew that I'd gone up because one of my triplets had died, because they all looked somewhat guilty. I think it was very unfair on them, as well as unfair on me, to have us in the same ward. I'd gone from being normal mummy to a bereaved mummy.

So we pulled the screens around us and then felt really ghastly about it. About two hours later, I was saying to Robert, I have just got to get strong now, and get back up there for the others. I was already working out how I could pull myself together. I just felt so sick when I stood up to get into the wheelchair, a lump of blood almost lobbed out of me on to the carpet. I felt so physically awful, and I didn't know how I could make myself get better. I wanted to force myself to sit up and get into the chair. I was really frightened about how ill I felt. I'm usually such a capable person, and I felt almost like a complete and utter invalid. I knew that I wanted to get back up there, but at the same time I was quite frightened about it.

Robert went out and phoned mother. I'd told him where she'd gone for lunch, and he told her that Megan had died. Mother then came rushing back from Islington, or wherever she'd been, at about two-thirty. They told me they'd leave Megan in this little room they've got off to the side, so that if we wanted to go back we could. I felt that I wanted to go back, and that I hadn't cuddled her enough and I hadn't been with her enough. And at that point a doctor came in and she pulled the curtain and I just knew from her face that something terrible had happened, and she said, 'I'm terribly sorry to tell you but Caitlin has just died'.

Unlike Megan, where we had a warning that her lungs were not going to hold, Caitlin's death was a *fait accompli*. At that point I don't think I could have been lower. I think also that when Megan died I'd assumed that was all that was going to happen. Nothing more could go wrong, surely – they were going to make it. The staff weren't being pessimistic, they weren't saying, 'These children don't have a chance.' They were just saying, 'You know, they are going to be very sick children, and you must accept that.'

But I didn't want to accept it because then it would be as if I was inviting the worst possible thing. After we went through all that with Megan – on the way back downstairs I said to Robert, 'Just let me look in at Isobel and Caitlin,' and I went over and Caitlin was all wrapped up with aluminium foil on her, and she had a little bonnet on her head, and I just took a look at her, and I said, 'Well, I'll be back for you just as soon as I can, but I've just got to go back downstairs.' I was just talking to her, saying, 'I'll see you later.' And it wasn't till later, and I felt awful that I'd been fussing about Megan.

I think this is probably what a lot of multiple birth parents go through whether the children live or not. You can't spread yourself around and physically I was slumped in a wheelchair, thinking I was going to fall off the wheelchair, as it was uncomfortable sitting up. I just wanted to lie down with my knees slightly pulled up, because of the pain and things, and I just wanted to get back downstairs. When I heard that Caitlin had died, I felt terrible that I must have glanced at her face while she was alive for a minute at the most.

The staff at the hospital were all brilliant. We went back upstairs, and by then they'd got Caitlin off all the machines and everything, and she was dressed, and we were in this room again, and there we were with our two daughters, and with one left. At that point, I said to Robert, 'I cannot cope if anything happens to Isobel, I just can't cope.' And we were saying, 'Look it won't, it just won't – she's going to be OK, and now let's be with these two.' I think that that was something I had read in a book, but it all came very naturally … the need to be with the children, to see them and to touch them, even though they were tiny. I know a lot of people find it easier to deny and say, 'I don't want to know'. A lot of women who have a stillborn child say they don't want to see them. But I think that there is this thing of regret afterwards if you don't spend time with them. So we spent about an hour or so in the room with the two of them, Megan and Caitlin; they were both tucked up in this little crib together, and it was the most awful thing to leave them, and they said they'd be there if I wanted to go back.

I said I'd seen Megan again. Megan was so tiny she became cold very quickly. That was a frightening reminder that there really was no life. It wasn't as if I'd had any impression of their personalities or anything – it was just a big void. And then I said to Robert, 'I'm not going back down to the ward,' and he said, 'No, we're not going.' He was completely behind me on that. I refused to go back down because I couldn't face going into a ward with people; I just wanted to be alone. And I certainly didn't want to be in a room with women and children. After that I think I was just terribly calm, because I was so tired, and physically absolutely and utterly whacked.

We went back to the bedroom which was opposite, in a little room to the side of the special care baby unit, and that was much better. I was given lots of painkillers. I had a weird reaction to them – I kept waking up thinking, 'I just want to be pregnant again – I want the children back in my stomach, not on the outside.'

What followed was a really weird five days in hospital with the children. Isobel was up and down and up and down. We were going to lose her on the first night and then she rallied, and then they had to do something, and then she rallied, and then she had a big collapse, and then physically she rallied. The doctors said, 'She's come through probably the worst of it but we're not happy with what she's been through.' With all the oxygen and tubes she had about four little lots of stitches on her body. Where they'd done something to her lungs, or where they'd repositioned tubes or little plasters there were scars. She just looked like a battlefield; she was such a fighter. She really just kept clinging on there, and we both felt afterwards that she'd done us proud.

Eventually they did a brain scan, and it showed she'd had a massive cerebral haemorrhage and there was really nothing they could do, and they got another doctor to give a second opinion. I think they did it for themselves as much as us really. This lovely paediatrician came and told us exactly what this meant, which was that basically one side of her brain was very badly damaged and the other side was very seriously damaged, and she was unlikely ever to have any quality of life. He could say with a great degree of certainty that she would be deaf and blind, that she'd be unable to have any motor skills, and she would probably be unable to walk. There was nothing that even I could cling on to as being good news.

We were told that on Thursday afternoon. By then my father had flown back, and my brother flew over from South Africa. Robert and I talked about it. We had decided with the doctors that the next time Isobel had a relapse, or another problem with a lung, we wouldn't fight it with all the machines and the rest of it; we would just let her go. And that was the decision. We'd realized that we were not going to be going home with a baby; we just sort of accepted that, and felt well, this is something that we can't do anything about.

By then she'd had so many ups and downs. Each day we'd come running through for her and if we weren't there the whole time there was someone else with her. But we knew that she was going down, and we'd go back and talk to her, you know, try and talk her out of it. Up until the time of finding out about her brain haemorrhage we were willing this tiny baby to make it, and then I was almost wanting her just to slip away.

On Friday the doctors came in and said to us, 'Our concern now is something that does happen occasionally, which is that we would have thought by now she would have had another relapse.' They said that, given that she'd had seven in the first two days, they expected she'd have gone. But physically all the signs were she was still rallying – everything seemed to be getting stronger. I thought, 'If only it had been like that at the beginning, but it isn't'. She had had seven of these lung collapses and a massive brain haemorrhage.

She was this little tiny baby in front of me – the smallest, smallest little dot, just lying there, and we knew that there was nothing that could be done to make her well. And so on Friday night my mother and father were staying at their club. When they left, Robert and I talked about it quietly, when we had time to ourselves to talk over what we should do. When they were going, dad came over and gave me a hug, and mother was going out and Robert was on his way back to see Isobel. When I was alone with dad I said, 'Dad, we're going to turn off her machine tonight.'

Which is what we did. Because we just felt at that point that she'd given us everything, given us a week, or six days to come to terms with it – and that it was inevitable. Keeping her alive at that time would be just selfish. But it's a pretty awful thing to have to do; an awful decision to have to make. But in a way, when I say it was a decision, it was really a non-decision. It might have happened anyway, three or four or five days later, but then they said she might have carried on for two weeks or so, and would have put everybody in limbo. And if that had happened, I wouldn't have felt particularly pleased with myself as a mother. And I don't think Robert would have felt he'd been a particularly good father.

It really wasn't like making a decision. They had showed us the scan, and showed us what a healthy brain looked like, and then showed us what Isobel's outline looked like, and pointed to the problems and explained everything to us very clearly. And, I said to Robert, 'the only decision we made from having those children, that we actually had to take, was to let Isobel go'. I had never made a decision such as what colour are we going to dress them in today, or what time shall I feed them, or should I change their nappies, or anything. But now I had to decide to let my baby die.

And what was really, really weird was that it felt the right thing to do. We knew what was coming, as in the situation with Megan. We waited until everyone went, and the hospital was really lovely – quiet and tranquil in the middle of the night. And we went in about two in the morning, and the nurses and doctors were the ones who had been on duty with us pretty much throughout; and they just quietly unwired and unplugged, and undid this and undid that.

So we just had our Isobel, which was really quite lovely. We wrapped her up, and went into another room, not the room we'd been in before – it was a little waiting room, and we just sort of held her and took her through. Robert went off after about ten minutes, and I said to him, 'Would you phone Dad? He said it didn't matter what time, just to let him know.'

At that time of night, there was no traffic, so they arrived in about fifteen minutes. When Robert went he said that he'd phone my parents and tell them that Isobel had died. But when he came back I said, 'Darling she hasn't died'. Her little heart was just fluttering away, and it was just lovely that we were so quiet and together. There was a bed and we all lay on the bed, each of us on either side and Isobel in between us. And then the next thing we knew, the door opened, and in came my parents, and all of us fell asleep, and Isobel just didn't wake up.

I was really surprised that in the midst of all of the horror, there was a tremendous calm, and we all actually went to sleep. Robert and I hugging her in the middle, so when my parents opened the door, there was just this tiny baby fast asleep in between us. And my mother was terribly upset obviously, well, all of us were. My brother was miserable, and Robert and I were sort of smiling and saying, 'It's OK, it's really OK'. Because I think that we knew we'd really done something – well, we hadn't done anything – but we'd made the right decision.

Helen had been rushed to the Royal London Hospital, where there were four neonatal cots available to receive the quads once they were born. She was desperately worried because one of the babies, she later called him Freddy, was in some distress. Jonathan had been warned that there was a possibility Helen would have to go into the intensive care ward after the operation because she was suffering from severe toxaemia. The last thing she remembered seeing was more than twenty medical people in the operating theatre waiting to take care of the babies. The operation was performed on the morning of Tuesday, 28 July 1989. Helen was taken to intensive care straight away. Octavia was born first, then Freddy, then Harry and Clemmie last.

The first memory I have I wasn't completely conscious because I couldn't see, everything was black. I just remember this overwhelming fear, it was like being in a black hole and there wasn't any end. I knew something dreadful had happened, but I didn't know what it was. I didn't know I was me and I didn't know I'd had any babies.

I don't remember the exact moment that I regained consciousness. I know that the second night I was in intensive care I was conscious enough to know about the babies. I was wheeled into their room on my bed from intensive care, which was very difficult for everybody because I was connected to so many things and obviously it was very cramped. By then I'd come off the ventilator, which is why I could be moved then. My sight had come back a bit by that stage.

I must have then lost consciousness and come round again. I still couldn't see and everything was black, but this time I knew who I was and that I'd had the babies. I could hear Michael Chapman's voice so I knew he was there but I couldn't see him. I remember waving my wrist to show that I wanted to write and then being able to feel that I had paper and although I couldn't see I knew what I wanted to write. I still have the piece of paper, it was given to me afterwards by Michael Chapman. It has on it three not four, three not four, and then boy.

I don't remember Michael Chapman answering my question; I'm sure he did but I don't remember it. When I was conscious enough to see and was wheeled in to see the children, I knew that Freddy was dead. I remember being very worried about him and asking the nurse who looked after me – Was he cold? Was he blue? She said that he was all right, that he was safe and that she had been told he was very beautiful. I kept worrying, saying well where is he, can I see him, I want to see him. They said not just then but that I would be able to. I was absolutely desolate; I couldn't, I just couldn't bear it.

I remember thinking so it's three not four and I thought well the three will be all right – I felt that they were all right because they were alive. I remember thinking, 'Oh well, I can die and I can go with Freddy because I don't want him to be on his own.' Jonathan said to me afterwards that at one stage through the night he didn't think that I would live – he always wondered if that was the time when I was dreaming about Freddy because I didn't want to live any more. I wanted to go and be with Freddy and I always feel cheated of Freddy.

When I came to see the children for the first time I could see light but I couldn't see people properly. I couldn't work them out spatially, they all seemed out of focus and very big. I was looking into the incubators and just saying things. I couldn't see them but I didn't want to admit this to other people. Although my sight had come back it wasn't real sight, it was light and shapes, nothing more. I did know I loved them, I knew they were there but I just couldn't see them properly. I kept trying to be sick and I couldn't breathe properly. I felt so ill.

Then I went back to intensive care. I felt better because I knew the babies were nearby. I was still worrying where Freddy was and I didn't want him to be cold. It wasn't until three or four days after the birth, when I came out of intensive care, that I held Freddy. He had lived for about ten or twenty minutes. He didn't resuscitate properly – when they got his heart going it wouldn't continue.

Poor Jonathan, I think it must have been awful for him to stand on one side of a door and look through a window and see that happening to his son. He must also have been very worried about me – it must have been terrible to have to watch someone you love in pain, to be a bystander and feel so impotent. I don't know what that was like for him, he's told me a bit but not very much.

Even though I was so ill and the babies were in incubators I felt I bonded with them immediately. It was instant – there before they were born. What I couldn't cope with was how ill they were. They were tiny – the size of my hand in length just to my wrist. I'd never seen such tiny babies and their skin was transparent; I could see the veins and the arteries through it. That was just indescribable – to see through your babies' skin to their internal being. I thought they were beautiful, they were our babies.

They were all ventilated. Octavia was the most ill for the first twenty-four hours. She couldn't maintain her body temperature properly. Both Clemmie and Harry were ventilated. It was the beginning of what would be described as classic neonatal problems.

The three crucial aspects of a premature baby's health are its ability to breathe, feed and control its temperature. All these factors are taken into consideration if the baby is nursed in a sterile incubator where the temperature is controlled, where the oxygen supply can be easily changed according to the baby's needs and where feeding can be achieved by passing a tube down the baby's nose into the stomach or by giving an infusion into the veins. The other function the incubator has is to reduce the risk of infection by providing a sterile environment because premature babies have a poor resistance to infection.

After that other complications came with head bleeds because the blood vessels in their brains are so fragile they burst and bleed very easily. That happened to all of them. Harry had the worst bleeds, he had two class four bleeds either side and then developed cysts, and Clemmie had a class three on one side and a class four bleed on the other side and developed a cyst – she had severe damage. When Octavia was ten days old she had a class one head bleed, which was the lowest in that classification. Because of these head bleeds they told me that the children wouldn't be 'normal' and would have disabilities. It was very hard because one baby had died and we were trying to accept that we were going to have three disabled children if they survived.

Head bleeds can be diagnosed by ultrasound scan. They are categorized by the area in which they occur and how extensive the bleed has been. The blood vessels in the brain rupture and then bleed into the ventricles. It is difficult to assess exactly how much damage these cause; it depends on the part of the brain.

I felt the paediatrician mishandled telling us. I was still unwell – in a wheelchair with a drip. We were taken into this horrible room which was all brown with revolting orange flowery curtains that were drawn – it was so hot I just wished they would open the windows, at least open the curtains. I thought if I can see out I won't feel so claustrophobic.

She told us that Harry and Clemmie had suffered head bleeds – we couldn't quite believe it because it was too much. She was saying that the head bleeds had this classification of four down to one but she didn't say specifically what our children had been classified as. I remember thinking, 'I know the answer to this but I have to ask,' and I said, 'Well which classification of bleed did Harry have?' and she said, 'Class four,' and I said, 'And Clemmie?' and she said a three and a four. I thought I knew it would be the worst, it would never be one and it would never be, 'No they haven't had any bleeds at all.'

I hate it when I feel I am given half-information. They didn't want to volunteer all the information; you had to drag it out, you had to ask. I think the training says to give a certain amount of information and if the patient or the patient's guardian, mother or father asks for more then it shows that they have an understanding, therefore they can be told more. I just find that so arrogant and so unhelpful because I'm sure they wrote down that we didn't handle being given this information very well because we got upset. I'm not surprised that we got upset but neither did they handle it very well; they could have given us more information in a more understanding and sympathetic way. It was very much, 'I'm the professional and you're a member of the public and you happen to be here.'

A few days later I was wheeled in to the room with the paediatrician again and she had an American psychiatrist with her. Jonathan was with me and they said, 'We've got an hour, we're going to talk about the babies and what's wrong with them and about the death of Freddy.' I just couldn't believe it, I thought, 'Well I've never met you, I don't know who you are, why should I come into this room and you decide that this is what I'm going to talk about? They haven't asked me if I want to talk about it.' I was so frightened that all the babies were going to die. I felt if I stayed with them and opened the portholes and held their hands then I would stop them dying. I always felt that if I could have held Freddy maybe he wouldn't have died. I'm sure there's no medical evidence of that but that's just a mother's instinct and a mother's love can do lots of things.

I said I wasn't going to speak. I felt trapped, I couldn't leave the room because I was in a wheelchair so I couldn't get out and I had to wait for someone to open the door to let me out.

That night they thought Clemmie was going to die. I had gone back to the room on the ward and they came to take me up in the wheelchair. The doctor told me how ill she was and that they had done absolutely everything they could for her and there was nothing more that they could do. The reason he'd asked me to come up was that I would want to be with her, but he also said that mother's and parents' love can take over where medicine leaves off – that he firmly believed. I held her hand. He was sitting on a stool on the other side of the incubator and he said, 'Look at the monitors and that's what you've done. She knows that you're her mother.' As I held her hand her heart rate was better and she survived that crisis and many more over the next five months.

I'd never thought I would cope with a disabled child. Before I was pregnant I always felt that I was such a selfish person and not strong. When I was told what was wrong with the children, I immediately felt as though we were all second-class citizens; that I was a second-class mother because I didn't have perfect normal children and that they were second-class because they weren't perfect and normal.

My own recovery was quite slow. I had problems with infections. After Freddy's funeral I was transferred to Guy's because my consultant obstetrician was from that hospital and he wanted to look after me himself.

Gradually I began to realize how ill I had been. One of the other obstetricians told me Michael Chapman had been a worried man. When I asked Michael about it he played it down.

The funniest thing was the cleaner. I think she was Brazilian. She had cleaned my room in intensive care. She thought I was a miracle. She told me I had gone, she said, 'You just weren't there you were completely in another world, you were grey, you didn't have any colour.' I had been fitting and she said, 'You were fighting in the bed, you were completely out of it.' After that she held me in awe – she was very religious. She was so funny because she told all the other domestics that basically I should have died and here I was.

I felt that I didn't know where God was. I can't understand why, why he took Freddy. I do believe in heaven and one day I will be with them. I just believe that so implicitly and that's what keeps me going in life – that belief, that surety that that's what will happen. Octavia believes it as well.

Around November the children were transferred to a less intensive ward as they started to get better. In the ward there was the intensive care room and the nursery or the going home room. This was the room that as parents all of us wanted to get to but in fact it could be the most frustrating room of all: quite often a baby spent longer in this room and they were no longer very ill but nor were they well enough to go home. Day after day it would be very minor problems compared to what had been wrong. It was quite frustrating and I found it the most difficult.

It was in early December that they all caught an infection, which was caused by a respiratory virus. They had to go back to intensive care and Harry had problems with his shunts, which actually became blocked. He had to keep being reincubated and reventilated. From December onwards all three children were together in one room.

A shunt is a device which some children need to help to drain fluid from the brain. Some babies, particularly premature ones, don't develop this function efficiently enough for themselves.

By this time we knew that Clemmie was severely damaged. We took the decision that she was not to be ventilated any more so she was in what they called a head box – a big perspex box that went over her head and obviously had a hole cut for her neck and oxygen and air were fed in through pipes. She couldn't breathe in air because she had extremely bad lungs, she had something called BPD (Broncho Pulmonary Dysplasia) which is something that's very common in very premature babies. When they are born their lungs are so immature and they don't have enough lubrication. It becomes a vicious circle because when they're ventilated, they ventilate under pressure, and although the ventilation now has improved a lot, it actually blows holes in their lungs. Her lungs were like a sponge. They were so damaged and they were full of holes, but she couldn't stop being ventilated because she would have died. On the other hand to have continued to ventilate her they would have had to use higher and higher pressures and that would damage the lungs more.

It was very difficult. I knew she was dying and I just came in and out every day and I was waiting for her to die. I was waiting for an overwhelming infection to do it and she just kept hanging on for much longer than anyone ever thought she would. She stopped absorbing her food. She was still being tube-fed and the agreement was that she would be fed and kept comfortable but they wouldn't intervene medically any more. When she died she died just after someone had suctioned her. I heard a gasping noise and I was so used to all the monitors I didn't have to look at them, I could hear by the sounds they were making that it was going to happen. I just felt it was too early, it was too soon and I didn't want it to happen, but I knew I couldn't stop it happening. The nurse called for the sister to come in. She put her arm round me and she said, 'It's now, Helen.'

We took all the leads off her and the monitors and she was in my arms and she took about six or seven breaths and then she stopped breathing. I told her how much I loved her and how I would always love her and how wonderful she was – I loved her so much – and I kissed her.

They told me afterwards that there had been a family in the room with their baby and they didn't leave, they stood and looked but I didn't see them; it was as though there wasn't anybody there, just me and Clemmie.

We made the decision we did because they showed us a scan of her brain and the damage was very apparent. They said she was blind – I'd never thought she was blind – and she was very paralysed. I knew if she'd lived I would never have been able to look after her because she would have been so disabled. It would have broken my heart not to look after her. Because I knew that she would have had such a sad life, I felt it was kinder to Clemmie to let her go. I still think that. I loved her so much. I think loving is letting go and letting her be free. It was right for Clemmie; it would have been selfish to keep her and I wouldn't have been able to cope with her. That wouldn't have helped Clemmie and nor would it have helped Harry and Octavia.

When Clemmie died it made me feel guilty but there was a relief which I hadn't felt with Freddy. I just felt cheated with Freddy but with Clemmie there was some relief and there was despair. She was so strong and I thought we had kept each other going. She was my anchor; I had to keep going for Clemmie and she was comforting and she was my friend and I did have a relationship with her. I held her every day of her life, apart from two days when she was very ill. I used to worry going down in the lift after I left her. I used to think, 'Well, what if she died now, I'm stuck in the lift, nobody could get to me.' I think that it was very loving of her to die in my arms and I felt it was as though she was showing that she knew she was loved, because I couldn't bear for her to die on her own in an incubator in a corner and she didn't. She died in my arms and I told her I loved her.

Laura and Robert left the hospital soon after Isobel had died. Returning to the house with no new babies was a terrible confirmation of what had happened.

That was really the real beginning of the horror. I think the time at the hospital was a pure grief – it was just dealing with the children, and what was going on with them. When we came out it was all muddy – it was anger and many other emotions, and Robert and I nearly fell apart.

It was utter hell. Robert and I went through Relate, and tried to get over the mutual bereavement that we felt. He wasn't really angry with me, but I found everything very difficult at that point – coping with the business failing, and coping with all the other things, coping with a house that was a tip, with a concrete mixer in the living room. It was just a pretty dire time.

I felt totally and utterly in despair, and yet six weeks later I was back working. People were probably saying, 'Isn't she doing marvellously' or whatever, and yet I was feeling quite awful. We had invited a lot of my friends to come and see Sarah during that week, when she was alive. I feel that was quite important, because otherwise it would have been easy for them to see it as a miscarriage.

The other big battle we had was with the funeral. We wanted to be able to drive the children down to the church where they were to be buried, near my parents-in-law, without having to involve undertakers. They were all in one tiny little coffin together. My father took a shawl that my mother-in-law had knitted and wrapped them all up, and then Robert had to get special clearance to take up the coffin himself. What they thought we would do with the bodies I don't know, but we were not supposed to take them. And yet these were our children. The very idea of a funeral car and everything else was abhorrent.

Then the other issue Robert fought and won was to actually get them registered to get birth and death certificates for them. Legally you don't have to register a child under twenty-eight weeks that has been born and died, because it's called a neonatal death. But to us it was just something that at the time was really important, to acknowledge that they had been three people that had lived.

It was like a victory when we were allowed to register them. I didn't get into the organization side of it at all. I was just very pleased that Robert and I could drive them to the cemetery ourselves. Robert had bought a Renault Espace, anticipating three children, so we took them down on the back seat.

I felt numb. Almost as if I was a character in a play, and I wasn't really me. This was all just happening around me. It was like being in a tunnel, with nothing to divert your attention outside. I was going through the motions, it was a very surreal time. I was hurting so badly, and angry.

We received some very good advice, both from Relate and from Elizabeth Bryan of the Multiple Birth Foundation. What helped was their optimism. I realized that so much of what we were going through was inevitable. Elizabeth warned us that it was just the beginning, and something like 90 per cent of couples who suffer any bereavement, whether it's of the life of a child through an accident or whatever, go through a terrible time in their relationship. You think it will pull you together, but actually it puts such a strain on any marriage when something that you both want so desperately doesn't come about.

Sometimes, weeks down the line, I could be working in the office all day, and feel a little bit OK about it and then realize that Robert had had a dreadful day about it, or vice versa. Your grief is never equally matched. Then you get angry with the other person for not understanding that you're going through a really bad day. I think Relate did help us – but it was learning to be honest about our feelings which made the difference.

First of all we would target our anger at each other. Then there was a deliberate silence. Even if we were talking, I was shifting away and I felt myself becoming like an island. This was easy to keep up because Robert was away so much. The business was being set up, the site had to be built, so of necessity he spent a lot of time away.

I felt really angry about that – I was in this house, which had a concrete mixer in the sitting room, it was disgusting – and I felt very angry about the fact that I was alone. When it got too bad, I'd go and spend two weeks with a girlfriend, while something was being done like a bathroom being put in. I just remember very long stretches of being in the house by myself, and just going to bed with the children's photographs really.

I wanted to be pregnant again straight away. I felt we could paper over that ghastly incident if I was pregnant; life would just go on. That's the way I began to see it. I think I'm quite an ambitious person, and it was almost as if that became the measure of success. I'd always made sure I never put a foot wrong, or failed in anything, yet I don't think you could get a bigger failing than what I went through. I couldn't have bodged up anything more if I'd tried.

I felt guilty. I kept thinking back to things I had done, like carrying the hoover upstairs, and wondering if that was why I had gone into labour. I felt cross with myself that I hadn't been more assertive about my needs at the time and had been running around after other people. Those things become indelibly etched on your mind – about exactly what you were doing that you shouldn't have been doing.

When we had gone through the process of having the girls by IVF we had frozen embryos. I knew I could go back and try again. I had one attempt in the April of the next year, 1990, which failed. That time the eggs were put back into my uterus after being thawed, just at the time that I would normally ovulate – so there was no drug cycle. It's a really good procedure, not at all invasive, it's just like having an IUD fitted. When it failed I wasn't as disappointed as I thought I might be. Deep down I knew I needed a bit of time to get my relationship with Robert sorted out. I went home to South Africa on a holiday on my own for a while and made a very positive decision that I wanted to try to work things out.

In the September we had another attempt. We were told, 'We've got three embryos that we've thawed – one of them looks very dodgy but the others look all right.' They decided they would only put two back. When I found out I was having twins I nearly died. It was not what I wanted at all. I was panicked for quite some time about having another disastrous multiple pregnancy.

I thought, 'I'm only five foot four and a bit – I'm not big enough or tall enough to carry twins,' but I talked to the consultant, and we were told, at eighteen weeks I think, that on the scan there was a boy and a girl. And that just made an enormous difference. I know there are only three options when you're having twins about what the sexes can be but I was really pleased. For the first time, at eighteen weeks, I started to feel totally excited.

Recent developments

Worldwide, one of the chief causes of death and long-term handicap in new born babies is premature birth. A full-term pregnancy is forty weeks and deliveries that happen before then are defined as preterm. In the UK there are about 800,000 babies delivered each year and about 5 per cent or 40,000 of these, are born prematurely.

Professor Stuart Campbell, of King's College Hospital, has been looking at the effect of nitric oxide gas in the body on blood flow to the womb, particularly looking at pre-eclampsia. Nitric oxide, which relaxes the smooth muscle of blood vessels, exists naturally in the body but is also produced from a drug called glyceryl trinitrate. GTN has been used for a hundred years for the relief of angina or chest pain.

The researchers applied patches, usually applied to the chest of angina sufferers, to women who were in preterm labour, and who were having frequent and painful contractions. The contractions of all the women were reduced in frequency and severity and on average the pregnancies were prolonged by twenty-four days. The side-effects were few but this was a study of only thirteen women so it would be difficult to use it as hard evidence. However, if more trials are carried out and show similar results and minimal side effects the patches could be a major contribution. (C. Lees, S. Campbell, E. Jauniaux, R. Brown, B. Ramsay, D. Gibb, S. Moncada, J.F. Martin, 'Arrest of preterm labour and prolongation of gestation with glyceryl trinitrate, a nitric oxide donor', The Lancet, *28 May, 1994.)*

CHAPTER 8

WHERE ARE THEY NOW?

For some women, a child resolves the crisis which the trauma of infertility brought into their lives. There is no magic answer to how to resolve the crisis if no babies arrive. Expressing the grief one feels for a child which never existed is extremely difficult and the outside world is not readily sympathetic.

In this chapter Miranda, Liz, Sheila, Vivienne, Laura, Rosemary and Helen reflect on the experiences they have described, and what they are doing now.

Miranda: At the beginning of the time Miranda contributed to this book she was recovering from a failed IVF attempt and trying to prepare herself to face going through it again. She told me she knew she was presenting a picture of herself as 'Mrs Adjusted' but that she was also experiencing moments of complete despair.

I think becoming thirty was a difficult time. For Clive and me, infertility has coloured the rest of our lives – it is the single worst thing that has happened and it has caused damage. I've seen Clive's confidence being eaten away and although other things have been difficult it is mainly the failure to have children which has undermined us both. I have lived with it long enough to be able to see a life in front of me without children but I don't think Clive is at that stage yet.

The last IVF attempt in the early spring of 1994 was successful. Miranda is now more than thirty weeks pregnant and the baby is expected just before Christmas. They are also about to move house for the second time this year. Miranda has taken things very easy during her pregnancy and it all appears to be going extremely well. Her homeopathy practice has lapsed a little simply because she is moving to a different area and will have to find new clients there.

I am really interested in what it feels like to be pregnant – I suppose because it is something I wanted for so long. I can imagine why it can be a really frightening experience for women who feel ambivalent about being pregnant – being taken over by a tiny parasite. The word parasite upsets people when I use it – but, I am just so thrilled, so happy, so delighted to have this little thing and I would gladly lie for nine months in a coma being a perfect host if that is what it required.

I do feel a bit superstitious. I don't like to talk about 'when I have a baby in December' and I wouldn't choose names. I think those are fairly natural anxieties, I don't think it is because it is an IVF baby. I can't bring myself to use the words to describe what would happen if it didn't all turn out to be all right. I try not to think about it. My largest emotion is optimism.

I feel a great excitement now when I see other women with their children. I really feel I am going to be joining that happy family. I think if a pregnancy had happened four years ago, without any of the disappointments and trauma, Clive and I would have taken having children in our stride. We have come closer and closer to an understanding of what having children means to us. The devastation of the thought that we would never have children, particularly for Clive who was so moved by the sight of the embryos which didn't become babies, has profoundly affected us.

I intend to continue with homeopathy and I would like to maintain an interest in infertility. I know about the hope, the bitter disappointment, the guilt and self-recrimination and the sense of being outside 'normal' family life. I also understand that there is nothing to be gained from blaming oneself for past actions or relationships. During the painful journey I made, the support of my homeopath and the influence of the remedies made it possible for my experience to be transformed into something valuable in my life. I hope I will be able to help my patients with a compassion gained from experience.

At Liz and Andy's consultation at the Queen Charlotte's hospital in London, the doctors said that Andy's sperm count seemed to be low and they needed him to masturbate twenty times over the next weekend. It was the last time they ever went to see a doctor about not conceiving. They both knew they were not going to be able to go through with any long-term medical treatment.

I am just about to hit my thirty-eighth birthday and I am not pregnant and not going to be pregnant, I suspect.

The thought of babies is never far away. I work in a public relations company in central London. Having started with a baby food manufacturer's account, all my new business appears to be about babies. I have the Baby Savlon account, also Baby Fresh Baby Wipes and a filing cabinet full of everything you ever wanted to know about breastfeeding. Because the company is full of women of child-bearing age there is always someone having a baby. I get a bit snappy occasionally when I feel overwhelmed by it but I think my colleagues understand. Also I am forever finding myself at thirty-eight years old staying late with all the 22-year-olds while my peers have gone home at six because of childcare commitments.

PR is not the be-all and end-all of my life. Where other people probably invest in their family Andy and I have done other things. I have learnt how to be a marriage guidance counsellor, we travel a lot and plan lots of holidays – a weekend in Madrid is not unheard of – and we go out and eat and talk to each other a lot. So our relationship does very well because we are able to nurture and cherish it. We also have lots of time for our families and our parents come and stay regularly.

I don't dread the future, I look forward to it. Sometimes I get a bit upset – the other day one of my colleagues became a granny at forty-eight and I had a twinge realizing that I would never be a granny.

I have never been followed up by the hospital. No one ever came and said, 'Are you still worried about your fertility?' My GP asked me if I was on the pill the last time I went to see him, so he has obviously forgotten I ever thought about it. I still fill out a menstrual chart every month but it is more to try to understand how I feel at different times of the month than anything else.

I went back to Queen Charlotte's in the summer to make a trial film for the television series of *Labours of Eve*. It was the first time I had been back and I had no idea how strongly I would react. The anger just welled up inside me and I poured out all my feelings of annoyance – the pomposity of the consultant, the tactless advice and the lack of any counselling. I found it very therapeutic. For a week or so afterwards I was walking around completely furious but it made me go back and reanalyse why I felt so strongly about it. I feel a lot better now than I did earlier this year. Generally I hope and believe that age helps.

In 1984 Sheila married at the age of thirty after following a career in teaching and having at that stage experienced no craving for a child of her own.

She tried for three years to have a child but despite her determination was unsuccessful. By the end her marriage was in pieces and eventually she and her husband separated. Sheila's husband went to live with the woman he had had an affair with who had by that time had his child. Sheila's life was shattered and two or three years after this time she felt she wanted to talk to other women about their experiences. The following is an extract from a letter she wrote to a magazine published by ISSUE, in an attempt to find other women with an unfulfilled desire for children.

'In retrospect I realize that the failure of the IVF was due to me refusing to face up to the fact that my marriage was disintegrating – within a year of it my husband had decided our marriage was over. By this time my anger against him had reached such a pitch that I was unable to respond appropriately and I smashed up the house and ended up in hospital for two days. Fortunately they did not give me a psychiatric label as they recognized the pain and hurt I was experiencing. I was now having to face life alone and re-evaluate what was important to me as everything which had been important had now been removed – my hope of a child, my husband and my career. This led me further into alternative therapies as I took up yoga, which introduced me to shiatsu and I am now trying to repair the emotional and physical abuse of the last eight years. My husband is now living with the woman he had an affair with, which is very difficult for me to accept because I still love him deeply and miss his company.'

After asking women with similar experiences to write she did receive several letters. During my own research for this book I have realized that there is very little in the way of support for women who have been unsuccessful and are no longer trying to overcome their infertility medically.

Sheila now teaches at a further education college. She is just forty and is not trying to have children, nor is she in a relationship. She is pursuing an alternative career as a psychotherapist.

For a long time I felt I was being punished. It felt to me that I had done all the things I could possibly have done. Whatever I did didn't seem to work and it felt as if my husband was punishing me. It might seem a bit irrational now, but I thought maybe I hadn't looked after myself when I was younger, or that I was a bad person. I became very negative.

As far as my status in the world as a woman goes, it was as if everything was turned upside-down for me. I began with the idea that women should work, and feeling sorry for women who didn't work. Now everything is reversed – I think women aren't valued enough and that motherhood isn't valued enough. I would advocate that women should be paid to stay at home, and that it's the most important job that women can do; there is too much pressure for women to stay at work and work is over-valued. My whole way of thinking has completely changed, which is strange since I haven't got a child and I do have to work.

I am taking a psychotherapy training course at the moment; we obviously have to have therapy ourselves. I realize that I am very angry with my body. I'm trying hard to change that view but it's not easy. It's almost like I have a love-hate relationship with it. There's one part of me that really feels angry, that thinks, 'What's wrong with this body?' Then there is a more loving, nurturing part, where I try to think of it as a friend to whom I would be really caring and loving. I'm trying to look at myself in that more nurturing way.

Although I have three lovely nieces and friends who do include me in their family life, I do feel an intense sense of isolation as though I am on the fringes of society. I also feel much of the literature that has been written about the subject of infertility is directed towards couples.

Vivienne had been diagnosed with pelvic inflammatory disease, which had developed shortly after she had a coil fitted. After several attempts to combat the effects of the inflammation with both antibiotics and surgery, she was posted to Hong Kong with her husband Chester. It was there in 1983 that she decided that she would go through with a hysterectomy, although she knew that she would have no chance of conceiving after it was done. She and her husband had briefly considered both adoption and surrogacy, but they were too old for adoption and Vivienne didn't want to put her twin sister at risk in a surrogacy arrangement.

In Hong Kong, Vivienne worked in the military nursing corps where she cared for the health of military families. She and Chester were later posted to Northern Ireland for a year. It was then that Vivienne felt, after nine years, that it was time for her to leave the military and she went to work on a special care baby unit. In 1987 Chester was coming to the end of his 23-year career in the military and they decided to set up a rest home for the elderly. They moved to North Yorkshire and ran a small home for five years. Vivienne feels they made this decision largely because they didn't have a family and she wanted to get away from maternity nursing.

The infertility had a profound effect on her feelings about herself. Her self-confidence was very low and she had gone from being a vivacious and sociable person to someone far more introverted.

In 1988 I went to my new GP. I told her, 'Each year I think I will come to terms with my infertility, but it is actually getting worse.' She recommended a really good psychologist. The therapy took a year: every week, then every fortnight. I really needed it. Although Chester and I are very close he had run out of ideas, and things to say to me. Then I used to shut off. I stopped sharing it with him because I thought, he's had enough of all this.

Once I had been to the psychologist, I didn't look back. I realized how my confidence had been eaten away. I could also see how frustrating it must have been for Chester – he was doing all he could, but I wasn't getting any better. I worried that I might drive him away. I tried to explain to him that it was not because I didn't love him but because I didn't love myself. I didn't even like myself because of my feelings of failure. When I was miserable I would wonder why he didn't go off and marry someone who could give him a baby. I knew deep down that he didn't marry me for children. I think if he had gone off I wouldn't have been surprised because I must have been very, very difficult to live with. I know that for a couple of years things were very tricky on the intimate side of things. But he was very understanding. I knew that I was very depressed, but I thought I could handle it. The psychologist told me that at the end of the day I had to shut the door on it.

Then something extremely important happened. I got called up to go to the Gulf War, because nurses were in short supply. It was very traumatic and off I went to Saudi Arabia. It was a great turning point – it boosted my confidence and was very challenging. I realized that life was so precious. We set up a hospital which was going to be the burns and evacuation unit at the airport terminal. They needed nine wards each with a hundred beds. We had to set the whole thing up with equipment installed in just three days. I worked in the casualty part and although there were obviously a lot fewer casualties than were at first expected we probably had about 360 cases through. Saddam Hussein was sending scud missiles over our heads into Riad.

I had stopped driving after my hysterectomy – somehow I just didn't have the confidence to get into a car. But in the desert I had to drive trucks around – it did me so much good. It was three months and Chester and I wrote every day. Sometimes you are able to put things on paper that you would never say to each other. Even on the phone we only had snatched conversations but those few minutes were so valuable.

When I came back we decided to close the business. We moved into the heart of the Yorkshire Dales to a wonderful house. Our cottage is attached to a house which belongs to a family from London. They wanted someone to live there and look after the house and them when they retreat from London. They specifically wanted a couple without children.

Around the time we moved I started to work in a police rehabilitation unit and got some basic qualifications in counselling. I find real satisfaction in my job, which is listening to people talking about their grief. I feel that all the other work I have done in my life was leading up to me doing this job. I feel I can help people so much. They don't know why I am able to help them but really it is because of what has gone on in my life over the last fifteen years that I am able to understand their feelings.

The combination of changing jobs and the Gulf War helped me to turn my life around. A couple of weeks ago a colleague had a baby and Chester and I went to see them. I used to get this terrible lump in my throat and I had to pretend to be happy for the mother. This was the first time I had found it any easier. I think that has come with getting older. We are now much happier about our lives and that helps enormously.

Christmas is a difficult time. I resist other people's families because it is too upsetting. We do everything that people who have children can't – we stay in bed and go for long walks.

One of the other things I used to find really impossible was small talk. The first thing that people always ask you is, 'Do you have a family?' The most useful piece of advice I have ever been given is a way of answering that question. Now when people ask me I say, 'Yes – I have a lovely husband, two cats and fifteen chickens'. I used to have to say no, and then what can other people do except look embarrassed or ask you why not. I can't tell you how much this has helped – it completely alters a situation I use to dread every day.

Laura now lives in Birmingham. She has a boy and a girl who were born in 1991 after two embryos were put back during her normal menstrual cycle. Her husband works in Wales, and consequently only gets home at weekends. Their house is being done up so they still live with a cement mixer in the kitchen occasionally. Laura's parents come to stay and take great pride in their wonderful grandchildren. The death of her first three children is still indelibly etched on Laura's memory but her present day life is full of the joys of young children.

The twins are now three and completely different from each other, but are both chirpy, happy and very entertaining company. I think that having the kind of experience I had makes you a different kind of mother. I'm sure every mother loves her children and has the same worries, such as, 'How would I manage without them?' But I don't think it is possible to go through the anxiety that you may never be a mother, or to have three babies and watch them die, and come out with the same emotions about them as any normal mother. I regard them as utter miracles.

The fact that the second time round we had a boy and a girl made us feel we were so lucky. It wiped out all that pain in one fell swoop. It took until they were six months old before I could accept they were going to stay. In the beginning I was so anxious they might be taken by a cot death or some infection, but I don't think that I'm overly protective or neurotic with them now. I'm not sure that someone who had children naturally would understand the gratitude I feel; I don't know who to direct it at but I just think, 'Thank God'. They are so special. Every weekend I say to Robert, 'I just think they are so brilliant. I am so lucky.'

I completely understand people who go through more complicated procedures than I did to become a mother. If I'd known when I was twenty-six what I know now about being a mother I would truly have gone through much more to achieve this. It is so incredible.

I think it will always have been an important experience that I went through. A friend asked me recently, 'What were the names of your girls?' I was still angry with her for forgetting, but if she had asked me a year or so ago I would have decked her. Something fundamental happened to me because my heart was broken by the whole experience. I think I am a slightly kinder person than I was before. At the time I felt hardened up completely because I couldn't afford to crack the shell which was so fragile. I was barely holding myself together and I could be very brittle. Now I am definitely much softer.

I also have to think, 'Well if the girls had lived then the twins would not be here.' I have a fatalistic view – if everything had not happened in exactly that order I wouldn't be here today listening to these two children having that conversation which gives me such pleasure. This makes sense of it. I would go through the whole thing again to be where I am now.

We mentioned to the children once that they had sisters who died but we don't talk about it yet because they are too young. We want to be completely up front with them about the deaths and about the technology side. We tease them about being the 'shiverers' because they came from the deep freeze (frozen embryos). They sometimes play in the room where the freezer is and we joke that they have a magnetic attraction to it. Robert sometimes says to them, 'Would you like us to have another baby?' and if he asks them where Mummy's babies come from they say they are in the freezer.

I have until next year to get the remaining embryos out. If it works on a natural cycle then we would like to have one more but we wouldn't go though the whole thing of collecting eggs again. The reasons for waiting are to do with work and going back to South Africa for Christmas and our financial constraints – all the things which shouldn't be important. But when you know the eggs are in the freezer you can be that much more clinical about it. Also I am much less driven than before because it is not my only hope of having a family.

I still do the same work in market research from home. I really appreciate the freelance life because I can be flexible about the time I spend with the children. Robert works in Cardiff and will do for the foreseeable future, so he is only at home at weekends. I do bereavement counselling for the Multiple Birth Foundation, so I talk to women who have been through similar experiences to me. I find it difficult sometimes to try to put myself back into that situation because I now feel my life has moved on from there. But I want to do it because I know that it is so important and painful for that person.

Rosemary has had more medical interventions than any of the other women in this book. In her twenties she had an operation called a presacral neurectomy, which may have affected her fertility later on. After microsurgery, which she described in Chapter 5, she went on to have one attempt at IVF. Although she did produce four healthy eggs which fertilized and were replaced in her uterus the pregnancy test was negative. She did briefly consider having another go but a routine smear test revealed that she was in the early stages of cervical cancer. A further operation was performed and part of her cervix was removed. She and David were then given very little reason to hope that any medical procedure would improve their chances of conceiving and Rosemary was told she would have even less chance of carrying a baby to full term.

It is now four years since the IVF attempt. Rosemary is working part-time running a creche. She is thinking about taking some more qualifications and going into the field of social work.

The last few years have been so absorbed with trying to have a baby that I have been left feeling, 'What on earth do I do now?' I originally went into teaching because I wanted to work in a caring profession so I suppose I want to do something which is more than just about earning money. I am not an ambitious person and I am not a career type at all, which means that work is not something I would turn to as an alternative purpose in life.

I am still only forty-four but I can honestly say I would never consider ever trying reproductive technology again. I am not objective and my view is coloured by the fact that nothing succeeded for me. But I have thought that if I had my life over again, with the knowledge I have now, I would have had nothing done at all. Before I always had the thought that maybe it would work but now looking back it just seems a lot of unnecessary trauma to have gone through for nothing.

My main regret is the presacral neurectomy operation in Harley Street. It is one thing which I cannot come to terms with. I still wake up in a cold sweat thinking, 'If only I hadn't agreed to have that done.' It was such a mistake on my part.

Other things have happened in my life which have caused pain but not having children is by far the worst. I have been able to talk through and gradually come to accept events that upset me in my childhood – through counselling or therapy I have even felt healed. But I will never, ever, until the day I die, come to terms with not having children because I can't change it and it is something that will never ever go away. I have no control over that.

I still have days when I sit at home and sob. I can't describe the grief and frustration. Most of the time it is bearable and as I get older I hope it will get better. But in some ways age cannot help – at the moment other people having their own children reminds me of my pain, in a few years they will be having grandchildren – another void to face. I am sure it will always be there.

Accepting that the grief will not go away is actually part of accepting the whole thing. I used to think that at some point in the future I will reach nirvana and there will be no more tears because the grief will have gone. I now believe that will never happen. On days when I feel down it overwhelms me and it is devastating. We live in a society where everything has to be right and happy and there is a general belief that you can always come out of these things but I personally don't believe that. I can see myself sitting and crying when I am seventy. I also think it is important to accept that unhappiness is a part of life too and you can't just bury it.

I have found counselling an enormous help. I can see that my expectations of what having a child might mean to me were unrealistic. I started by feeling it would solve my confusions about my identity and I have come to realize that was something I had to do for myself. I did eventually meet my biological mother and it was an extraordinary experience.

I was extremely nervous and anxious about whether she would like me. Over the years I had built up a picture of what she would be like in my mind and needless to say she was nothing like that. It is impossible for me to describe what I felt like the moment I met her – we just stared at each other. After all those years of not knowing, actually seeing her did help me to come to terms with that part of my life. I had solved a lot of that already through counselling and therapy but to sit and actually see my mother made a great difference. David said we looked very alike and there were even little mannerisms which we share.

We haven't developed an incredibly close relationship and meeting her didn't suddenly supply me with an instant sense of shared family history but it solved something and it definitely helped. I am still very happily married to David.

Helen is still living in South London although she is about to move to the country. The two remaining children from her multiple pregnancy are Harry and Octavia. They are completely delightful children as seen on the programme that was made for the *Labours of Eve* television series. Although Harry has hydrocephalus, cerebral palsy, hearing problems and a language and communication disorder, he has achieved far more than anyone ever expected. Octavia has far fewer problems and is in a mainstream school. Both children had to be fed through tubes to their stomachs as a result of their prematurity; Octavia is now fully able to feed herself but Harry still needs to be fed by tube during the evening. Helen's own health is extraordinary considering the stress of the last few years. She had another baby, without treatment, in February 1993. She and Jonathan have separated.

It concerns me very much that I had been a private patient, who paid money for fertility treatment, and it was the NHS that picked up the tab when things went wrong. I have felt so guilty about that. Octavia and Harry are now six. Over those years it was the National Health Service that dealt with the disaster. Private medicine has not helped at all. The expertise, certainly for neonatal facilities, isn't in the private sector. The obstetricians and other necessary experts are all trained and working in the NHS – particularly in the teaching hospitals.

I think this is all wrong but I'm very glad that the NHS is there for my children. The whole point of the NHS is that regardless of your ability to pay it is free. Harry needs it to live. If his equipment was taken away from him he would not survive.

Private medicine doesn't seem to give a lot back. Children like Harry couldn't be in the private sector – they wouldn't make a profit. He is a loss maker and they're not interested in loss. The idea of trying to privatize the NHS fills me with dread – my children cannot be seen in terms of cost-effectiveness. I had quite a battle to get them with their present GP because the practice is fundholding and they do not want children like Harry and Octavia as patients because they use up quite a large amount of their budget each month.

Since they were small I have been a full-time nurse and I come pretty cheap. If I estimate my worth on Harry's disability living allowance and the invalid care allowance it works out at 70p an hour and I don't have a pension or any holidays. I had to go into hospital about two years ago and it was the first time I had left the children. Jonathan said that when Octavia came home from nursery school that day she couldn't believe that I wasn't there. I was always there and when he came to see me in the evening in hospital he said they just completely expected me to be at home. Octavia was opening the cupboard doors to see where I was hiding. I have had to be there more than most mothers have purely because of their needs. When Harry first came home he was on his drip feed for all but an hour each day. We only had that hour to get out of the house.

Retracing the last few years of my life in order to make the *Labours of Eve* documentary programme has been quite a difficult experience. It has brought back things which are very painful. I've had some of the dreams that I used to have. One of them is particularly horrible – I'm in the sea and I'm on a raft. I know something bad has happened. I've got the four children and the raft won't hold all of us and Jonathan's there too. He comes off the raft first because he says that I can look after the children and he isn't needed. He just slips away into the water and then I have to make the choice and it's always that two children have got to go. It's just such a horrible, horrible dream and I refuse to make the choice in the dream but it happens anyway and when the children float off it's Freddy and Clemmie and they look how they did when they died. I just hate that dream.

I hadn't dreamed it for a long time. I used to dream it a lot when the children were at Great Ormond Street. Harry was very ill and we thought he was going to die. I always felt that Harry wasn't safe on the raft and that the dream might end with only Octavia and me.

At different times since the children were born Jonathan and I have been offered counselling. We've refused it. I've always felt that in the professionals' eyes we carry a black mark against us because of our refusal. We said very pointedly that we didn't want to and they didn't seem to understand us. We felt that if we did talk to anyone it would be to our friends and to each other. Grief is so individual, it isn't necessarily a shared emotion and we felt that the people we were supposed to talk to didn't understand us. So why would we choose them to open our hearts to about such painful and unhappy experiences.

I felt very strongly that Octavia and Harry were alive and they had very special complex demanding needs and I had to give to them. We felt that Freddy and Clemmie would understand that and they wouldn't want it any other way – their brother and sister were alive and needed to be looked after and they needed all our love. That's where we channelled all our energies. To spend time talking about something that had happened, and was so painful, seemed pointless in the face of that. We hadn't talked to each other, why should we talk to anyone else? They didn't seem to understand it and the only people who did were the Multiple Birth Foundation and they said that all parents of multiple births said exactly the same thing.

The transition to being a mother was not a private experience for me. I felt I was being watched because my children were always in hospital wards. I sometimes felt criticized for having such set routines. But that was how I coped. The health professionals couldn't understand me which I thought showed their lack of sensitivity. I would have thought it was fairly obvious that my routine was all I had to hang on to because when children are in hospital they aren't just yours. They were mine in that I'd given birth to them and was their mother, but all the things that a mother naturally does were taken away because there was always a barrier – there was either an incubator window in front of me or there were tubes or a nurse. I was never on my own with my children.

I did feel very resentful of that – simple things like wanting to teach the children about night and day. In a neonatal unit they're like little battery chickens, they're in constant light and the noise never stops. I knew they would need to know about real things when they came home. I missed out on all the quiet moments that are just part of your life with a small baby at home. We were all on display. Even when we took them out of the incubators there were always people there.

The sad experiences I have had since I had children have taken an immense personal toll. It has changed me, my values have changed totally. I feel quite ashamed when I think of the values I used to have and my attitude to people in certain situations.

When Ascot was on this year I was thinking about the times I used to go. It would be impossible for me to go now – not just because of my childcare commitments and my financial situation but because I wouldn't fit in. I'd be very out of place, I wouldn't have anything to say to anybody. They wouldn't be interested in my life. If I asked my old acquaintances what they had been doing it would be various parties they'd been to, whether they were going to Bembridge this year and so on. I never see those people now because my life is so different and if I talked to them about the lack of physiotherapy or speech therapy in special schools it wouldn't mean anything. I think they'd find it rather embarrassing and want me to be quiet.

The experience of having Quinta has been so different. Her name means fifth born. I can't explain why I suddenly conceived without any help. Perhaps we were more relaxed but I doubt that because it was at a time when our marriage was under considerable strain. I don't know why we didn't conceive all the other times. I think she has helped in the healing process. She is different. She is Quinta and she's brought us normality.

Although at times she looks like Freddy or Clemmie and she brings back those memories, they're very positive, warm memories. There's nothing sad about Quinta. There's no way she is a replacement for Freddy and Clemmie. She is a completely different and wonderful baby with her own character – but the same stubbornness as the other two. I remember one of the paediatricians saying he couldn't believe what tough babies I'd got. They all fought so hard to be here.

Voluntary Organizations

AMARANT TRUST
Grant House
56-60 St John Street
London
EC1M 4DT
071 490 1644
To promote a better understanding of the menopause and hormone replacement therapy.

ASSOCIATION FOR POSTNATAL ILLNESS
25 Jerdan Place
London
SW6 1BE
071 386 0868
To advise and offer support to women suffering from postnatal depression.

BABY LIFE SUPPORT SYSTEMS (BLISS)
17-21 Emerald Street
London
WC1N 3QL
071 831 9393
To ensure that no baby suffers death or handicap at birth or immediately after through lack of appropriate care. Support for parents whose children are in a special baby-care unit.

BIRTH CONTROL TRUST
27-35 Mortimer Street
London
W1N 7RJ
071 580 9360
To promote the optimum provision of birth control services within the NHS.

BRITISH PREGNANCY ADVISORY SERVICE (BPAS)
Austy Manor
Wooton Wawen
Solihull
West Midlands
B95 6BX
0564 793225
FAX 05642 4935

BROOK ADVISORY CENTRE
153a East Street
London
SE17 2SD
071 708 1390
Education, advice and practical help in matters of sex and contraception.

CHILD
PO Box 154
Hounslow
Middlesex
TW5 0EZ
081 893 7110
To promote improved care and treatment of infertility.
To provide counselling facilities.
24-hour answering service.

HUMAN FERTILIZATION AND EMBRYOLOGY AUTHORITY
Paxton House
30 Artillery Road
London
E1 7LS
071 377 5077
Regulatory body for reproductive medicine.

INFERTILITY ADVISORY CENTRE RESEARCH FOUNDATION
15 Berkeley Street
London
071 224 4724
FAX 071 224 4725
To give advice via a hotline at any time about any aspect of infertility.
Provides treatments including AI & AID, GIFT and all infertility
investigations.

ISSUE
(National Fertility Association)
509 Aldridge Road
Great Barr
Birmingham
B44 8NA
021 344 4414
To offer advice, support and information to people with infertility
problems.

THE MISCARRIAGE ASSOCIATION
c/o Clayton Hospital
Northgate
Wakefield
Yorks
WF1 3JS
0924 200799
Information and support for women and their families after miscarriage.

MULTIPLE BIRTH FOUNDATION (MBF)
Queen Charlotte's & Chelsea Hospital
Goldhawk Road
London
W6 0XG
081 748 4666
To give professional support to families with twins, triplets etc and to educate professionals and the public on the needs of multiple birth families.

NATIONAL INSTITUTION FOR PARENTS OF PREMATURES
PO Box 1553
Wedmore
Somerset
0934 733123
To provide information and support networks.
Bereavement groups.

PRE-ECLAMPSIA (PETS)
Bryn Mor
Carmel
Caernarvon
Gwynedd
LL54 7AB
0286 880057
Acting as self-help and support group.

PROGRESS
(Campaign for Research into Human Reproduction)
27-35 Mortimer Street
London
W1N 7RJ
To support and protect research into the early stages of human development and the prevention of infertility.

STILLBIRTH & NEONATAL DEATH SOCIETY
28 Portland Place
London
W1N 4DE
071 436 5881
To offer support to parents bereaved through late pregnancy loss, stillbirth or neonatal death.

SUPPORT AFTER TERMINATION FOR ABNORMALITY (SATFA)
29-30 Soho Square
London
W1V 6JB
071 439 6124
To give support to parents when an abnormality is detected in their baby.

TWINS AND MULTIPLE BIRTHS ASSOCIATION (TAMBA)
PO Box 30
Little Sutton
South Wirral
L66 1TH
051 348 0020
Helpline – 0732 868000 (weekdays 6–11pm; weekends 8am–11pm)
To give encouragement and support to parents of twins, triplets or more. To advance education and research on the needs of multiple birth families.

WELLBEING
27 Sussex Place
Regent's Park
London
NW1 4SP
071 262 5337
FAX 071 724 7725
To fund medical research into gynaecology and obstetrics for the better health of babies and children.

Index